Exam Practice
A LEVEL

A Level
Exam Practice

Covers AS and A2

Chemistry

Authors

John Sadler

Rob Ritchie

Contents

AS and A2 exams

Different types of questions

We have mainly used two types of questions in this exam practice book: structured questions and extended answers.

Structured questions

The main type of question you are likely to meet in a unit assessment is the structured question. These questions consist of an introduction, sometimes with data, followed by three to six parts, each of which may be further sub–divided. The introductory data provides the major part of the information to be used, and indicates clearly what the question is about.

- Make sure you read and understand the introduction before you tackle the question.

- Keep referring back to the introduction for clues to the answers to the questions.

Structured questions usually start with easy parts and get harder as you go through the question. Also you do not have to get each part right before you tackle the next question.

Extended answers

This type of question requires you to write several sentences in your answer. They are often used to assess your ability to communicate ideas clearly and logically.

Other questions

In addition to structured questions and questions requiring extended answers, synoptic assessment also uses free-response and open-ended questions. These questions allow you to select your own examples and develop your own answers. Multiple-choice questions are used more rarely.

What examiners look for

- Examiners are obviously looking for the right answer, however it does not have to match the wording in the examiner's marking scheme exactly.

- Your answer will be marked correct if it contains all the main facts. You do not get extra marks for writing a lot of words.

- You should make sure that your answer is clear, easy to read and concise.

- You must make sure that your diagrams are neatly drawn with a ruler and labelled.

What makes an A, C and E grade candidate?

Obviously, you want to get the highest grade that you possibly can. The way to do this is to make sure that you have a good all round *knowledge* and *understanding* of Chemistry.

A grade candidates have a wide knowledge of chemistry and can apply that knowledge to novel situations. They are equally strong on all of the modules. The minimum mark for an A grade candidate is 80%.

C grade candidates have a reasonable knowledge of chemistry, but they are unsure about applying their knowledge to novel questions. They have weaknesses in some of the modules. The minimum mark for a C grade candidate is 60%.

E grade candidates have a limited knowledge of chemistry and have not learnt to apply their ideas to novel situations. They find it hard to memorise definitions and facts. The minimum mark for an E grade candidate is 40%.

Successful revision

Revision skills

- Try to do your revision in the same place and at about the same time every day
- Always start with a topic with which you are familiar
- Stop before you get too tired.
- Leave something easy with which to start your revision the next day.
- Try using post-it notes to keep track of your revision and highlighter pens to emphasise important points in your notes.
- Soothing background music can help
- Don't stay up late the night before an exam trying to learn new topics. You will have forgotten most of it by the morning and the lack of sleep will probably affect your performance in the exam.

Practice questions

This book is designed to help you get better results.

- Look at the grade A and C candidates' answers and see if you could have done better.
- Try the exam practice questions and then look at the answers.
- Make sure you understand why the answers given are correct.
- When you feel ready, try the AS and A2 mock exam papers.

If you perform well on the questions in this book you should do well in the examination. Remember that success in examinations is about hard work, not luck. Thomas Edison said that genius was 1% inspiration and 99% perspiration.

Planning and timing your answers in the exam

- You should spend the first few minutes reading through the whole question paper.
- Answer the question you think you can do best first. The easiest question is usually the first question on the examination paper.
- There is no need to write out the question, it wastes time and space.
- Use the mark allocation to guide you on how much to write. The number of lines is usually the number of marks for the question + 1.
- You should aim to use one minute for each mark; thus if a question has 5 marks, it should take you 5 minutes to answer the question.
- Plan your answers; do not write down the first thing that comes into your head. Planning is absolutely necessary for free–response/extended answer questions.
- Try and allow time to read through your answers. Do not cross anything out at this stage unless you are changing the answer you have given. Examiners can only mark what you have written down. Any answer is better than no answer.

How to boost your grade

- Learn the definitions – these are easy marks in exams and they reward effort and good preparation. If you want to boost your grade, you **cannot** afford to miss out on these marks – they are very easy to get.

- Always give the full definitions, remember that in many definitions temperature and pressure are important, and so state them.

- Always include state symbols and units, particularly in questions on thermochemistry and electrochemistry. *(s) for solid, (l) for liquid, (g) for gas and (aq) for a solution in water.*

- Always write balanced equations including state symbols. This is one of the ways chemists communicate information. Make sure you use the right symbols in your equations. *For reversible reactions ⇆, equilibrium reactions ⇌ and reactions that go in one direction only →.*

- Make sure that the equation you have written does take place and balances. Ionic equations should be used where appropriate. In some equations, particularly those in organic chemistry, you can use [H] to represent a reducing agent and [O] to represent an oxidising agent.

- Learn a set method for solving a calculation and use that method. You will then be in a far stronger position for tackling any numerical problems.

- Check any calculations you have made at least twice, and make sure that your answer is sensible.

- Make sure that you are familiar with all the functions on your calculator and that you know how to key in positive and negative indices.

- Learn to interpret the answers displayed by your calculator: *A calculator display of 4.2^{-02} means 4.2×10^{-2} or 0.042.*

- Never borrow a calculator for an examination. Often keys need to be pressed in different orders with different makes and types of calculator. Borrowing will lead to confusion and mistakes.

- Make sure you know the difference between number of decimal places and number of significant figures. *25.696 to one decimal place is 25.7 and to 4 significant figures it is 25.70.*

- For numerical calculations, always include units.

- Always show the sign for enthalpy changes and oxidation numbers: *e.g. calcium has an oxidation number of +2.*

- Do not give ions as names of reagents. $Cr_2O_7^{2-}$ is NOT a reagent. *The reagent is potassium dichromate(VI).*

- Draw diagrams with a ruler or some other aid. Label with straight lines. Make sure that the apparatus you have drawn is safe (e.g. that it is not completely sealed) and that the apparatus you have drawn is 'real' apparatus.

- Give complete colour changes. The test for an alkene is **NOT** that bromine turns colourless, but *the colour change is from brown to colourless.*

- Write chemical names legibly. *If you spell ethanal as ethanæl it will be marked wrong.*

- Read the question twice and underline or highlight key words in the questions. *e.g. in **terms of covalent bonding** suggest why nitrogen is **less reactive** than chlorine.*

- Remember that conditions of a reaction are very important *e.g. whether a concentrated or a dilute acid is required.* Heating is not the same as heating under reflux which involves the use of a condenser.

- Use the periodic table and other data that you are given. *Don't try to remember data such as relative atomic masses.*

- You must represent the formulae of organic compounds correctly, so make sure you know the difference between empirical, molecular, structural, displayed and skeletal formula.

- Your graphs must be correctly labelled, have a suitable scale so that it fills the graph paper and that the best line is drawn through the points. When plotting graphs, make sure that you include fully labelled axes and units.

Questions with model answers

C grade candidate – mark scored 8/14

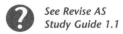 *See Revise AS Study Guide 1.1*

In terms of atomic structure, give **one** similarity and **one** difference between each of the following pairs of substances: **[7 × 2]**

Examiner's Commentary

(a)   A proton and a neutron

Protons and neutrons both have the same mass ✔, *a proton has a charge of +1, a neutron has no charge* ✔.

(b)   A proton and a hydrogen atom

They both have one proton ✔, *the proton has a positive charge* ✘. ⟵ *Hydrogen has one electron, a proton has no electrons.*

(c) $^{12}_{6}C$ and $^{14}_{6}C$

They have the same number of protons (6) ✔, *but a different number of neutrons (6 and 8)* ✔.

(d)   O and O^{2-}

They have the same number of protons (8) ✔, O^{2-} *has two extra electrons* ✔.

(e) Cl^{-} and Cl^{+}

They have the same number of protons ✔, Cl^{+} *has more electrons* ✘. ⟵ Cl^{-} *has 18 electrons, Cl^{+} has 16 electrons.*

(f) Na^{+} and F^{-}

They are both ions ✘ *but have different charges* ✘. ⟵ *True, but this is NOT the answer in terms of atomic structure. Both have the same number of electrons (10), but a different number of protons.*

(g) $^{55}_{25}Mn^{2+}$ and $^{56}_{26}Fe^{3+}$

They are both transition metals ✘ *but have different charges* ✘. ⟵ *Again true, but you have not answered the question. They have the same number of neutrons and electrons but a different number of protons.*

Questions with model answers

A grade candidate – mark scored 8/11

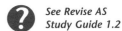 *See Revise AS*
Study Guide 1.2

Examiner's Commentary

(a) Electrons have very small masses and they are negatively charged. Give one other property of electrons. **[1]**

They spin ✔.

Electrons spin on their axes, clockwise and anticlockwise. These are represented by ↑ and ↓.

(b) Which noble gas has no 'p' orbitals? **[1]**

Helium ✔.

(c) Listed below are the electronic configurations of 5 elements, R to V. One of the configurations is wrong. **[9]**

R $1s^2\ 2s^2\ 2p^6$ U $1s^2\ 2s^2\ 2p^4\ 3s^1$
S $1s^2\ 2s^2\ 2p^6\ 3s^1$ V $1s^2\ 2s^1$
T $1s^2\ 2s^2\ 2p^6\ 3s^2\ 3p^6\ 3d^5\ 4s^1$

(i) Identify the element with the wrong electronic configuration and, assuming that the number of electrons are correct, write down its correct electronic configuration.

U: $1s^2\ 2s^2\ 2p^5$ ✔.

(ii) Which element is a noble gas?

R ✔.

(iii) Which **two** elements are in the same group of the Periodic Table?

S and V ✔.

Elements in the same group have the same number of electrons in their outermost shell.

(iv) Identify element T.

Cr ✔.

(v) Why is the 4s sub-shell filled before the 3d sub-shell?

The 4s sub-shell is in a lower energy state than the 3d sub-shell ✔.

(vi) Suggest why T has the structure shown and not $1s^2\ 2s^2\ 2p^6\ 3s^2\ 3p^6\ 3d^4\ 4s^2$.

The 4s sub-shell is in a lower energy state than the 3d sub-shell ✗.

Half-filled shells are more stable.

(vii) Divide the elements R to V into s block, p block and d block elements in the Periodic Table.

s block: S,U,V ✗*; p block: R* ✗*; d block: T* ✔.

Remember that U is incorrect and is in the p-block (see (i) above).

Exam practice questions

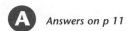 *Answers on p 11*

(1) The table gives the electronic configuration of consecutive elements in each of two groups (**A** and **B**) of the Periodic Table.

Group **A**		Group **B**	
Element	Configuration	Element	Configuration
T	$1s^2\ 2s^1$	X	$1s^2\ 2s^2\ 2p^4$
V	$1s^2\ 2s^2\ 2p^6\ 3s^1$	Y	
W		Z	$1s^2\ 2s^2\ 2p^6\ 3s^2\ 3p^6\ 3d^{10}\ 4s^2\ 4p^4$

(a) In which group of the Periodic Table are: **[2]**

     (i) T, V and W

     (ii) X, Y and Z?

(b) Write down the electronic configuration of

     (i) W

     (ii) Y.   **[2]**

(c) For the electron in $3s^1$, what is meant by 3, s and 1?   **[3]**

(d) How many pairs of electrons are there in   **[2]**

     (i) V

     (ii) Z?

(e) What is meant by an 'orbital'?   **[2]**

(f) Element V reacts with element X to form a compound.   **[3]**

     (i) What is the formula of the compound formed between V and X?

     (ii) What type of bonding would you expect in this compound?

     Give a reason for your answer.

Exam practice questions

(2) The diagram below shows the first ionisation energies of the elements in the third period of the Periodic Table.

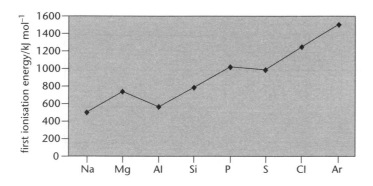

(a) The electronic configuration of silicon can be written as
[Ne] $3s^2 3p_x^1 3p_y^1$ **[3]**

 (i) In terms of electron configuration, what does [Ne] represent?

 (ii) Using the same format, write down the electronic configurations of Mg and S.

(b) Explain, including an equation with state symbols, the meaning of *first ionisation energy*. **[4]**

(c) State **three** factors that affect ionisation energy. **[3]**

(d) Sketch, including approximate values, the first ionisation energies of the elements carbon to aluminium in the Periodic Table. Explain the shape of your sketch. **[2]**

Answers

(1) **(a)** **(i)** Group 1 **(ii)** Group 6

Examiner's tip

*To find the group, add up the electrons in the highest principal quantum number. In group **A** there is only 1 electron and in group **B** there are 6 electrons.*

(b) **(i)** W is $1s^2\ 2s^2\ 2p^6\ 3s^2\ 3p^6\ 4s^1$ **(ii)** Y is $1s^2\ 2s^2\ 2p^6\ 3s^2\ 3p^4$

(c) 3 is the principal quantum number ; s is the sub-shell ; 1 is the number of electrons in the sub-shell.

(d) **(i)** 5 **(ii)** 16

Examiner's tip

Each orbital can hold 2 electrons. There is one s orbital that can hold 1 pair of electrons, three p orbitals that can hold 6 electrons (3 pairs); five d orbitals that hold 10 electrons (5 pairs) and seven f orbitals that hold 14 electrons (7 pairs). The orbitals in a sub-shell are occupied singly before pairing starts.

(e) A region around an atom where there is a high probability of finding an electron at any moment in time.

(f) **(i)** V_2X

(ii) Ionic; electrons transferred from V to X to obtain noble gas structures.

(2) **(a)** **(i)** $1s^2\ 2s^2\ 2p^6$

(ii) Mg is $[Ne]3s^2$ and S is $[Ne]3s^2\ 3p_x^2\ 3p_y^1\ 3p_z^1$

(b) The first ionisation energy of an element is the energy required to remove **1 electron** from each atom in **1 mole** of **gaseous atoms** to form 1 mole of **gaseous 1+ ions**. $E(g) \rightarrow E^+(g) + e^-$

Examiner's tip

The key words are in bold.

(c) atomic radius; nuclear charge; electron shielding (screening)

(d)

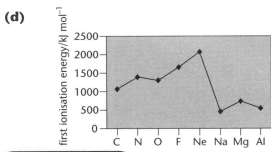

C to Ne have similar shape to Si to Ar on question paper, but values are higher because the electrons are nearer the nucleus.

Examiner's tip

Note, the last three elements in this graph were the first three elements in the question.

Questions with model answers

C grade candidate – mark scored 6/10

 *See Revise AS Study Guide 2.3*

(a)   Find **(i)** the empirical formula and **(ii)** the molecular formula, of a gaseous compound X containing 85.7% of carbon and 14.3% hydrogen. (M_r = 56. A_r : H, 1.0; C, 12.0)   **[4]**

Examiner's Commentary

(i) Molar ratio of atoms C $= \frac{85.7}{12} = 7.14$;
and H $= \frac{14.3}{1} = 14.3$ ✔

Always divide by the A_r.

Divide by smallest C:H = 1:2
Therefore the empirical formula is CH_2 ✔

(ii) Each CH_2 unit has a mass of 14 ✔

Number of units $= \frac{56}{14} = 4$

Molecular formula is C_4H_8 ✔

(b)   Write the equation, including state symbols, for the complete combustion of X.   **[2]**

$C_4H_8(g) + 6O_2(g) \rightarrow 4CO_2(g) + 4H_2O(l)$ ✔✔

Complete combustion always gives CO_2 not CO.

(c)   Compound X is an alkene. All alkenes have the formula C_nH_{2n}. Why do all alkenes have the same percentage composition?   **[1]**

Because they contain the same number of carbon atoms ✗.

The percentage will always be $\frac{12n}{14n} \times 100 = 85.7\%$
The M_r of C_nH_{2n} = $12 \times n + 2 \times n = 14n$.

(d)   If 7.0 g of ethene (C_2H_4) molecules react together to give 0.00025 moles of poly(ethene) (C_2H_4)$_n$ as the only product, calculate the number of carbon atoms in a molecule of poly(ethene).   **[3]**

✗ ✗ ✗

Number of moles of ethene $= \frac{7}{28} = 0.25$
(M_r of ethene $= 2 \times 12 + 4 \times 1 = 28$)
Since 0.00025 moles of polyethene is obtained from 0.25 moles of ethene then 1 mole of polyethene will be obtained from $\frac{0.25}{0.00025}$ moles of ethene = 1000 moles.
Since each mole of ethene contains 2 carbon atoms, the number of carbon atoms in a molecule of poly(ethene) = 2000.

A grade candidate – mark scored 8/10

See Revise AS Study Guide 2.1

(a) **(i)** What instrument is used to measure relative atomic mass? **[1]**

Mass spectrometer ✔.

(ii) Naturally occurring magnesium consists of 78.6% ^{24}Mg, 10.1% ^{25}Mg and 11.3% ^{26}Mg. Calculate to three significant figures, the relative atomic mass of naturally occurring magnesium. **[2]**

$$\frac{24 \times 78.6 + 25 \times 10.1 + 26 \times 11.3}{100} ✔$$

$= 24.327$ ✗

> **Examiner's Commentary**
>
> *You have confused three significant figures with three decimal places (24.3).*

(b) When magnesium burns in air, a mixture of magnesium oxide and magnesium nitride (Mg_3N_2) is formed. Magnesium nitride is a white solid. Write the equation, including state symbols, for magnesium reacting with nitrogen. **[2]**

$N_2(g) + 3Mg(s) \rightarrow Mg_3N_2(s)$ ✔ ✔

(c) Magnesium nitride reacts with water to give magnesium hydroxide and ammonia. The equation for this reaction is

$Mg_3N_2(s) + 6H_2O(l) \rightarrow 3Mg(OH)_2(aq) + 2NH_3(g)$

(i) How would you show that ammonia gas was given off? **[1]**

It turns damp litmus paper blue ✔.

> *Ammonia can always be recognised by its characteristic pungent smell.*

(ii) What volume of ammonia (at r.t.p.) would be liberated if 2.018 g of magnesium nitride were added to excess water? (A_r : Mg, 24.3; N, 14.0) **[3]**

1 mole of Mg_3N_2 gives 2 moles of ammonia (48 dm^3) ✔

Number of moles of Mg_3N_2 used is $\frac{2.018}{100.9} = 0.02$ moles ✔

Volume formed $= 48 \times 0.02 = 0.96$ dm^3 ✔

> *One mole of gas at r.t.p. occupies 24 dm^3.*

(iii) Suggest why the volume of ammonia given off is much less than this value. **[1]**

The reaction did not go to completion ✗.

> *The water was in excess, so the reaction would have gone to completion. Ammonia is very soluble in water.*

Exam practice questions

A Answers on p. 16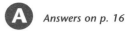

(1) The mass spectrometer is used to measure the relative atomic masses of elements and the relative molecular mass of molecules. Its three main functions are to:

- ionise the sample
- separate the ions in the sample in terms of their mass-to-charge ratio
- collect and detect the ions and measure their relative abundance

(a) **(i)** Will the sample be a gas, liquid or solid when it enters the mass spectrometer? **[1]**

(ii) How are the ions formed in the mass spectrometer?

Write an equation for the formation of M^+ from a sample M. **[2]**

(iii) After ionisation the ions are accelerated. How are the ions accelerated? **[1]**

(iv) Circle the ion which will be deflected the most

$^{20}Ne^+$, $^{21}Ne^+$, $^{22}Ne^+$, $^{20}Ne^{2+}$, $^{21}Ne^{2+}$ or $^{22}Ne^{2+}$.

Give a reason for your answer. **[2]**

(v) Why are very low pressures used in the ionisation chamber? **[2]**

(b) The diagram below shows the mass spectrum for naturally occurring gallium (Ga).

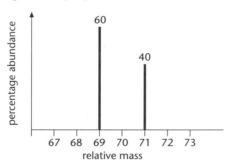

Calculate the relative atomic mass of naturally occurring gallium. **[2]**

(c) Br has two isomers ^{79}Br and ^{81}Br. If Br_2 is used in the mass spectrometer there are three peaks of Br_2^+ at 158, 160 and 162. Which species are responsible for these peaks? **[1]**

(2) One of the impurities present in fuels is hydrogen sulphide (H_2S).
Hydrogen sulphide burns to form sulphur dioxide and water.

(a) **(i)** Construct the equation for the combustion of hydrogen sulphide. **[1]**

(ii) What volume of sulphur dioxide (in dm^3) at r.t.p. will be formed
when 102.3 kg of hydrogen sulphide is completely burnt?
(A_r : H, 1.0; S, 32.1) **[3]**

(b) One way of removing sulphur dioxide is to pass it through calcium hydroxide
solution.

$$Ca(OH)_2(aq) + SO_2(g) \rightarrow CaSO_3(aq) + H_2O(l)$$

The solubility of calcium hydroxide in water is 1.85 g dm^{-3}.

(i) How many moles of calcium hydroxide dissolve in 1 dm^3 of water? **[1]**

(ii) What volume of sulphur dioxide can be absorbed by 100 dm^3 of this
calcium hydroxide solution at r.t.p.? **[2]**

Answers

(1) (a)(i) A gas

   (ii) The sample is bombarded with electrons.
   $$M(g) + e^- \rightarrow M^+(g) + 2e^-$$

   (iii) By using an electric field.

   (iv) $^{20}Ne^{2+}$ It has the smallest $\dfrac{mass}{charge}$ ratio.

   (v) To avoid other particles being ionised, such as oxygen and nitrogen molecules.

(b) $\dfrac{69 \times 60 + 71 \times 40}{100} = 69.80$

(c) $^{79}Br^{79}Br^+$; $^{79}Br^{81}Br^+$, $^{81}Br^{81}Br^+$

(2) (a)(i) $2H_2S(g) + 3O_2(g) \rightarrow 2H_2O(g) + 2SO_2(g)$

   (ii) 102.3 kg = 102 300 g.
   Number of moles of H_2S = $\dfrac{102\ 300}{34.1}$ = 3000

   3000 moles of sulphur dioxide will be formed
   = 3000 x 24 = 72,000 dm^3

(b)(i) Number of moles of $Ca(OH)_2$ = $\dfrac{1.85}{74}$ = 0.025 moles

   (ii) Number of moles used = 0.025×100 = 2.5 moles
   Volume of gas absorbed = 2.5×24 = 60 dm^3

Questions with model answers

C grade candidate – mark scored 6/10

See Revise AS
Study Guide 3.1

The atoms in molecules of chlorine and oxygen are held together by covalent bonds.

Examiner's Commentary

(a) What is meant by the term 'covalent bond'? **[2]**

A covalent bond is a shared ✔ *pair of electrons* ✔.

*Don't forget **pair** of electrons.*

(b) Using 'dot and cross' diagrams, show the electronic arrangement in molecules of

(i) chlorine   **(ii)** oxygen. **[2]**

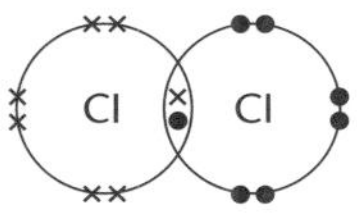

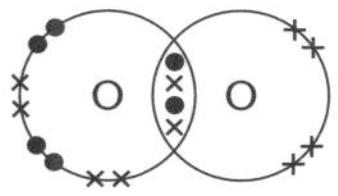

There must be 8 electrons in the outermost shell. You must distinguish between the electrons from each atom (dot and cross).

(c) The diagram below shows the covalent bonding in nitrogen.

In terms of covalent bonding, suggest why nitrogen is less reactive than oxygen and chlorine. **[1]**

Because it has fewer electrons in its outermost shell ✘.

Triple covalent bonds are harder to break that single or double bonds.

(d) Water is the hydride of oxygen. Explain why water has a higher melting point than the hydride of sulphur. **[1]**

Water has hydrogen bonding ✔.

Other inorganic compounds with hydrogen bonding are hydrogen fluoride and ammonia.

(e) The hydride of nitrogen is ammonia.

(i) Draw a dot and cross diagram to show the bonding in ammonia. **[1]**

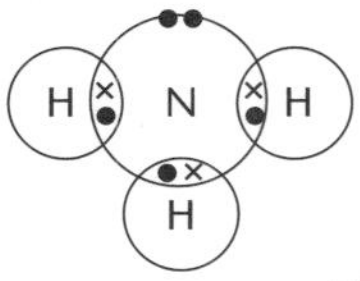

(ii) Explain, with the aid of diagrams, the formation of the ammonium ion NH_4^+ from ammonia and a hydrogen ion H^+. **[3]**

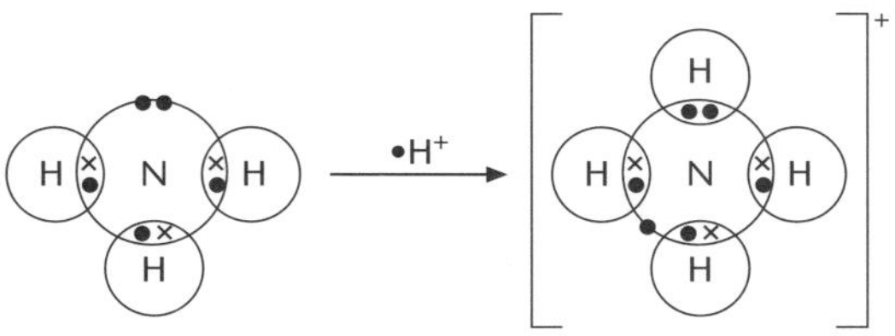

You have drawn a hydrogen atom and given the ammonium ion an extra electron. The hydrogen ion has no electrons and it forms a dative covalent bond with ammonia. (See Study Guide 3.1.)

Questions with model answers

A grade candidate – mark scored 11/16

 See Revise AS Study Guide 3.1 and 3.2

When hydrogen chloride is added to water, the following reaction occurs:

$H_2O(l) + HCl(g) \rightarrow H_3O^+(aq) + Cl^-(aq)$

(a) Draw the structure of (i) the Cl^- ion and (ii) the H_3O^+ ion. **[2]**

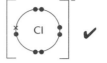 ✔ 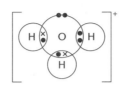 ✔

Examiner's Commentary

Chlorine has gained an electron.

(b) Use these structures to explain the meaning of :

(i) covalent bond **(ii)** dative covalent bond. **[4]**

(i) A covalent bond is a shared ✔ pair of electrons ✔.

(ii) A dative covalent bond is one in which one of the atoms ✔ supplies both ✗.

You have forgotten to say 'supplies both of the shared electrons'.

(c) When ammonia (NH_3) is added to water, the following reaction occurs:

$NH_3(g) + H_2O(l) \rightleftharpoons NH_4^+(aq) + OH^-(aq)$

Use a dot and a cross to show the structure of the OH^- ion. **[2]**

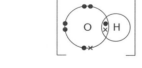

✔ ✗

You need to show the extra electron in a different way, e.g. ○ .

(d) **(i)** Name the ionic compound formed when hydrogen chloride reacts with ammonia. **[1]**

(i) ammonia chloride ✗.

It should have been ammonium chloride.

(ii) Draw a diagram to show the arrangement of electrons in the compound you have named in **(d)(i)**. **[3]**

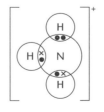

✔ ✗ ✔

You have forgotten to show the fourth hydrogen atom in NH_4^+.

(e) What are the shapes of the following: **[4]**

(i) hydrogen chloride **(ii)** water **(iii)** ammonia **(iv)** H_3O^+?

(i) linear ✔ (ii) V-shaped ✔ (iii) pyramidal ✔ (iv) triangular ✗.

H_3O^+ is also pyramidal – O is surrounded by 4 pairs of electrons.

Exam practice questions

Answers on p. 21

(1)   The theory of shapes of molecules was developed by Nyholm and Gillespie. They stated that 'electron pairs, whether in bonding orbitals or lone-pair orbitals, arrange themselves to be as far apart from each other as possible'.

    (a)   What do you understand by **(i)** bonding orbitals, **(ii)** lone-pair orbitals?   **[2]**

    (b)   Look at the following molecules: **[6]**

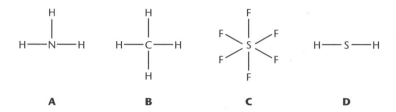

        (i) Which molecule has the greatest number of bonded pairs of electrons?

        (ii) Which molecule has the greatest number of lone pairs of electrons around the central atom?

        (iii) Identify the shape of each of the molecules and state whether it is planar or non-planar.

    (c)   The ion NH_2^- is found in compounds such as sodium amide.   **[6]**

        (i) Draw a diagram showing the outer electronic structure of the nitrogen atom.

        (ii) Draw a 'dot-and-cross' diagram to show the arrangement of the outermost electrons in NH_2^-.

        (iii) State, with reasons, the shape of the NH_2^- ion. Your answer should give an approximate value for the H–N–H angle.

Exam practice questions

(2) The table below gives some values for electronegativity on the Pauling scale.

C	N	O	F
2.5	3.0	3.5	4.0
Si	P	S	Cl
1.8	2.1	2.5	3.0

The value for hydrogen is 2.1.

(a) What is meant by electronegativity? [2]

(b) The hydrogen fluoride molecule can be written as $H^{\delta+}$—$F^{\delta-}$. It is a polar molecule and has a dipole moment. [3]

(i) What do the symbols $\delta+$ and $\delta-$ represent?

(ii) What is meant by a polar molecule?

(iii) What is meant by 'has a dipole moment'?

(c) Using only the elements in the above table of electronegatives and hydrogen, complete the following table. (The first one has been completed for you.) [5]

Description	Example	Shape	Polar bonds	Has dipole moment
pentatomic molecule	CCl_4	tetrahedral	yes	no
diatomic molecule	F_2			no
tetratomic molecule		pyramidal		yes
	CO_2	linear	yes	
triatomic molecule	H_2O		yes	
		octahedral		no

Answers

(1) (a)(i) A pair of electrons, shared between two atoms, in the same orbital.

(ii) A pair of electrons in the same orbital, not involved in bonding.

(b)(i) C: sulphur hexafluoride.

(ii) D: hydrogen sulphide.

(iii) A: pyramidal, non-planar.   B: tetrahedral, non-planar.
C: octahedral, non-planar.   D: V-shaped (non-linear), planar.

Examiner's tip

When defining shapes, the lone pairs are ignored. Read the question carefully. Sometimes you are asked how the pairs of electrons are arranged: the answer for both ammonia and hydrogen sulphide would be tetrahedral.

(c)(i) $\cdot \overset{\cdot\cdot}{\underset{}{N}} \cdot$

(ii) $\left[H \overset{\cdot\cdot}{\underset{\circ\circ}{N}} H \right]^{-}$
└─ electron from metal

(iii) V-shaped (non-linear), four pairs of electrons would arrange themselves tetrahedrally. Two are lone pairs and therefore non-linear. The angle will be between 104° and 106°.

Examiner's tip

The shape of NH_2^- will be very similar to that of water. Non-bonded pairs of electrons repel one another more than bonded pairs. Hence the angle is less than the tetrahedral angle of 109.5° or 107° from one non-bonded pair of electrons.

(2) (a) It is a measure of the attraction of an atom in a molecule for the pair of electrons in a covalent bond.

(b)(i) They represent a small positive charge and a small negative charge.

(ii) One where the electrons in the bond are shared unequally.

(iii) A molecule that will move when placed in a magnetic field.

Examiner's tip

For a molecule to have a dipole moment, the bonds must be polar and the molecule must not be symmetrical. (Its value is calculated by multiplying the charge by the distance between the atoms.)

(c)

Description	Example	Shape	Polar bonds	Has dipole moment
pentatomic molecule	CCl_4	tetrahedral	yes	no
diatomic molecule	F_2	*linear*	*no*	no
tetratomic molecule	NH_3	pyramidal	*yes*	yes
triatomic molecule	CO_2	linear	yes	*no*
triatomic molecule	H_2O	*non-linear*	yes	*yes*
heptatomic (7 atoms) molecule	SF_6	octahedral	*yes*	no

Questions with model answers

C grade candidate – mark scored 6/10

 See Revise AS Study Guide 4.2 and 4.5

Iron is made by the reduction of iron ore, haematite, with coke. Haematite contains iron(III) oxide (Fe_2O_3).

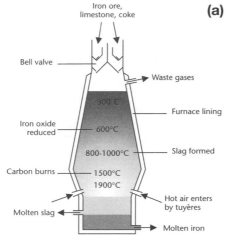

Iron ore, limestone, coke
Bell valve
Waste gases
300°C
Furnace lining
Iron oxide reduced
600°C
800-1000°C — Slag formed
Carbon burns — 1500°C
1900°C
Hot air enters by tuyères
Molten slag
Molten iron

(a) The diagram shows a cross section of a blast furnace.

(i) Why does carbon burn to form carbon monoxide, rather than carbon dioxide, at the base of the furnace? **[1]**

There is incomplete combustion due to lack of oxygen. ✔

(ii) The melting point of iron is 1540°C and that of iron(III) oxide is 1460°C. Construct the equation, including state symbols, for the reduction of iron(III) oxide by carbon monoxide. **[2]**

$Fe_2O_3(s) + 3CO(g) \rightarrow 2Fe(s) + 3CO_2(g)$ ✔ ✗.

The temperature for the reduction is 800°C. At this temperature, iron is a solid.

(iii) Why do the waste gases contain sulphur dioxide and nitrogen? **[2]**

The iron contains sulphur impurities ✔
and nitrogen is from the air ✔.

(iv) Suggest **one** advantage of slag floating on top of the iron. **[1]**

It keeps the iron molten ✗.

It prevents the hot air reacting with the molten iron.

(b) The air entering the base of the furnace is heated by the waste gases. Give **two** advantages of heating the air in this way. **[2]**

Hot air speeds up the reaction ✔ *and it is more economical because energy is saved* ✔.

(c) Another reaction in which iron is formed is **[2]**

$2Fe_2O_3(l) + 3C(s) \rightarrow 4Fe(l) + 3CO_2(g)$

In terms of oxidation number, explain why this is a redox reaction.

Iron is reduced from +6 to 0 ✗ *and carbon is oxidised from 0 to +2* ✗.

Iron is reduced from +3 to 0 and carbon is oxidised from 0 to +4. Oxidation numbers are stated for one atom only. Oxygen is always −2 (except in F_2O); therefore all other elements, when they combine with oxygen, have a positive oxidation number.

A grade candidate – mark scored 8/10

See Revise AS Study
Guide 4.1 and 4.3

Examiner's Commentary

The table below gives some information about elements in Group 1 and Group 2.

	Group 1			Group 2		
	Li	Na	K	Be	Mg	Ca
Electronegativity	1.0	0.9	0.8	1.5	1.2	1.0
Ionic radius/nm	0.068	0.098	0.133	0.030	0.065	0.094
Boiling point/°C	1330	890	774	2477	1110	1487

(a) Why are Groups 1 and 2 known as the 's block' elements? **[2]**

Their electronic structures end in either s^1 ✔ or s^2 ✔.

Groups 3, 4, 5, 6, 7 and 0 are the p block elements.

(b) Why are the metals in Group 1 known as the alkali metals? **[1]**

They react with water to form alkalis ✔.

Group 2 are known as the alkaline earth metals.

(c) Why does the atomic radius decrease across a period but increase down a group? **[3]**

Across a period the nuclear charge increases, thus increasing the attraction between the nucleus and the outer electrons. ✔ Extra shells are added down a group and these are further from the nucleus. ✔ The more shells the greater the shielding ✔ (both contribute to a decrease in the attraction between the nucleus and the electrons).

(d) Suggest why the boiling point:

(i) decreases going down Group 1 **[2]**

The strength of a metallic bond decreases down a group – the ions get larger and hence the attraction of the 'sea of electrons' to the nucleus decreases. ✔

(ii) increases across a period

More electrons contribute to the 'sea of electrons', the charge on the metal ion is greater and the ion is smaller ✔ (thus increasing the attraction).

(e) The action of heat on lithium compounds is similar to the action of heat on magnesium compounds. The reason is that both lithium ions and magnesium ions have high charge densities. **[2]**

(i) What is meant by charge density?

It is the charge on the ion ✗.

It is the ratio of charge on ion : atomic radius. The larger this value, the more it will cause large anions to decompose.

(ii) Lithium carbonate decomposes to give lithium oxide and carbon dioxide. Write the equation for the action of heat on lithium carbonate.

$LiCO_3(s) \rightarrow LiO(s) + CO_2(g)$ ✗.

Lithium is in Group 1.
$Li_2CO_3(s) \rightarrow Li_2O(s) + CO_2(g).$

Exam practice questions

Answers on p. 25

(1) Fluorine is the first member of Group 7, the halogens. It is the most reactive halogen. When it reacts with elements it can bring out their highest oxidation number (which is also the group number of the element).

   (a) Name **one** element that does **not** react with fluorine. **[1]**

   (b) Write down the formula of the compound formed between the following, in which the first named element has its highest oxidation number. **[2]**
   (i) boron and fluorine   **(ii)** sulphur and fluorine.

   (c) What is the oxidation state of oxygen in F_2O? Explain your answer. **[2]**

   (d) Fluorine reacts with water to give hydrofluoric acid and oxygen. Write the equation for this reaction and state, with reasons, what has been oxidised and what has been reduced. **[3]**

   (e) Give **two** reasons why fluorine has a lower boiling point than chlorine. **[2]**

   (f) Suggest why hydrogen fluoride has a much higher melting point and boiling point than the other hydrogen halides. **[2]**

   (g) Suggest how fluorine could be manufactured from sodium fluoride. **[1]**

(2) The table below gives information about elements in Period 3 of the Periodic Table. Use this information to answer the following questions.

	Sodium	X	Aluminium	Silicon	Y	Sulphur	Chlorine
Atomic number	11	12	13	14	15	16	17
Relative atomic mass	23	24	27	28	31	32	35.5
Boiling point /°C	890	1110	2470	2360	473	445	−34.7
Electrical conductivity	good	good	good	slight	poor	poor	poor
Formula of chloride	NaCl		$AlCl_3$	$SiCl_4$		S_2Cl_2	Cl_2

   (a) For elements **X** and **Y**: **(i)** Write their symbols, **(ii)** Suggest the formulae of their chlorides. **[3]**

   (b) What is the electronic structure of element 14 in terms of s and p orbitals? **[1]**

   (c) What type of structure is present in **(i)** sodium, **X** and aluminium **(ii)** silicon **(iii)** **Y**, sulphur and chlorine. Give reasons for your answer. **[6]**

   (d) The relative molecular mass of **Y** is 124. What is its molecular formula? **[1]**

   (e) Sodium reacts with hydrogen to form a white solid, sodium hydride (Na^+H^-), m.p.= 800°C. **[2]**
   (i) What type of bonding is present in sodium hydride?
   (ii) What is the oxidation number of hydrogen in sodium hydride?
   (iii) If molten sodium hydride is electrolysed, what product would be formed at the anode?

Answers

(1) (a)   Any noble gas except xenon.

(b)(i) BF_3 **(ii)** SF_6

(c)   +2 Fluorine is the most electronegative element, so it always has an oxidation number of -1; this makes the oxidation number of oxygen +2.

(d) $2F_2(g) + 2H_2O(l) \rightarrow 4HF(aq) + O_2(g)$
The fluorine has been reduced, oxidation number reduced from 0 to -1. The oxygen has been oxidised, oxidation number increased from -2 to 0.

(e)   Fluorine has fewer electrons and weaker van der Waals forces.

(f)   Hydrogen bonding. Hydrogen fluoride is a polar molecule with a lone pair of electrons on F, which is highly electronegative.

(g)   Electrolysis.

(2) (a)(i) Mg and P.   **(ii)** $MgCl_2$ and either PCl_3 or PCl_5 .

(b) $1s^2\ 2s^2\ 2p^6\ 3s^2\ 3p^2$

(c)(i) Giant metallic. They have a high boiling point and conduct when solid.

(ii)   Giant atomic. It has a high boiling point, and is a semi-conductor.

(iii) Simple molecular. They have a low boiling point and do not conduct.

(d) $\frac{124}{31} = 4$ P_4.

(e)(i) Ionic   **(ii)** -1 **(iii)** Hydrogen

Questions with model answers

C grade candidate – mark scored 7/12

See Revise AS
Study Guide 5.2

Examiner's Commentary

(a)   State Hess's Law   **[3]**

If a reaction can take place by more than one route ✔ *and the initial and*
final conditions are the same, ✔ *the total enthalpy change is the same for*
each route ✔.

(b)   In the diagram below, give the formulae of **X** and **Y**.   **[2]**

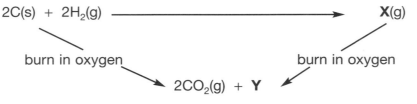

$2C(s) + 2H_2(g)$ ————————————————→ **X**(g)

burn in oxygen   burn in oxygen

$2CO_2(g) + $ **Y**

X *is C_2H_4* ✔ **Y** *is H_2 hydrogen* ✗.

Hydrogen, in the presence
of oxygen, always forms
water.

(c)   The standard enthalpy change of combustion of carbon
is −394 kJ mol⁻¹, and that of carbon monoxide is −111 kJ mol⁻¹.

Calculate the standard enthalpy change of reaction for:

$$2C(s) + O_2 \rightarrow 2CO(g)$$ **[3]**

$C(s) + \frac{1}{2}O_2(g)$ ———————— ΔH_r ————————→ CO

−394   −111

$CO_2(g)$ ✔

$\Delta H_r + (-111) = -394$ ✔ $\Delta H_r = -283\ kJ\ mol^{-1}$ ✗.

You have forgotten that
the reaction was for the
production of 2 moles of
CO. Answer =
−566 kJ mol⁻¹.

(d)   The enthalpy change of combustion of magnesium is
−602 kJ mol⁻¹. Would you expect magnesium to burn in
carbon dioxide to form magnesium oxide and carbon?
Explain your answer.   **[4]**

The equation would have been:
$2Mg(s) + CO_2(g) \rightarrow 2MgO(s) + C(s)$ ✔
but carbon dioxide does not support burning ✗ ✗ ✗.

You should have used the
enthalpy change of
combustion of carbon to
show that the reaction is
−810 kJ mol⁻¹ exothermic,
and is therefore likely to
take place.

A grade candidate – mark scored 8/10

*See Revise AS
Study Guide 5.2*

(a) The average healthy person needs 12 500 kJ from sucrose
($C_{12}H_{22}O_{11}$) a day. The enthalpy change of combustion of
sucrose is -5670 kJ mol^{-1}. How many kilograms of sucrose
(to three decimal places) are eaten each day? **[3]**

M_r of sugar is 342 ($12 \times 12 + 22 \times 1 + 11 \times 16$) ✔
5670 kJ is produced by 342 g ✔
12 500 kJ is produced by $\frac{342 \times 12500}{5670}$ *= 754 g = 0.754 kg* ✔

> *Remember many foods contain sugar.*

(b) It is too dangerous to measure the enthalpy change for the reaction:

$ZnO(s) + Mg(s) \rightarrow Zn(s) + MgO(s)$

It is also difficult to measure the enthalpy changes of combustion of
zinc and magnesium. The enthalpy change can be worked out
indirectly by a series of experiments. One of the experiments
would be to work out the enthalpy change for the reaction:

$MgO(s) + 2HCl(aq) \rightarrow MgCl_2(aq) + H_2O(l)$ reaction 1

(i) Write the equations for the other experiments you would
carry out. Show how you would use the results to calculate the
enthalpy change for the reaction between zinc oxide and
magnesium. **[3]**

$ZnO(s) + 2HCl(aq) \rightarrow ZnCl_2(aq) + H_2O(l)$ ✔ *reaction 2*
$Mg(s) + ZnCl_2(aq) \rightarrow MgCl_2(aq) + Zn(s)$ ✔ *reaction 3*
*add together the enthalpy changes for 2 and 3 and subtract those
for 1* ✔.

> *This is an application of Hess's Law where an energy change can be calculated indirectly.*

(ii) Why cannot the enthalpy change for

$CuO(s) + Mg(s) \rightarrow Cu(s) + MgO(s)$

be calculated by a similar method? **[1]**

Because CuO does not react with hydrochloric acid ✗.

> *Copper does not react with hydrochloric acid.*

(c) The reaction below is used to weld together sections of railway
lines.

$2Al(s) + Fe_2O_3(s) \rightarrow 2Fe(s) + Al_2O_3(s)$

The standard enthalpy changes of formation of Fe_2O_3 and Al_2O_3 are
-836 kJ mol^{-1} and $-1\,664$ kJ mol^{-1} respectively.

(i) Calculate the standard enthalpy change of this reaction. **[2]**

Enthalpy change = $-1664 - (-836)$ ✔ *= -828 kJ mol^{-1}.* ✔

(ii) Suggest why this reaction can be used to weld materials made
of iron. **[1]**

Iron is formed. ✗

> *The energy produced is sufficient to melt the iron.*

Exam practice questions

 *Answers on pp. 30–31*

(1)

Definition of enthalpy change	Type of enthalpy change	Enthalpy change
required to break and separate 1 mole of bonds in the molecules of a gaseous element or compound so that the resulting gaseous species exert no forces upon each other	bond enthalpy	**A**
B	standard enthalpy change of neutralisation	−ve
C	standard enthalpy change of combustion	**D**
when one mole of a compound in its standard state is formed from its constituent elements in their standard states under standard conditions	**E**	usually +ve

(a)   Identify **A**, **B**, **C**, **D**, and **E** in the above table.   **[8]**

(b)   The enthalpy change for the reaction $2Mg(s) + O_2(g) \rightarrow 2MgO(s)$ is $-1\,204$ kJ mol⁻. What will be the value for the enthalpy change **E** of magnesium oxide? Explain your answer.   **[2]**

(c)   What is meant by the standard state for an element?   **[2]**

(d)   **(i)**   The standard enthalpy change of neutralisation for the reaction between aqueous sodium hydroxide and hydrochloric acid is the same as for the reaction of aqueous potassium hydroxide and nitric acid. Explain why this is so.   **[3]**

   (ii)   Suggest why the value is less exothermic for the reaction between hydrofluoric acid (a weak acid) and sodium hydroxide.   **[1]**

(2) The bond energies, in kJ mol^{-1}, below, show the successive energies required to break the bonds in methane, water and carbon dioxide.

methane		water		carbon dioxide	
H_3C-H	+425	$HO-H$	+494	$OC=O$	+531
H_2C-H	+470	$H-O$	+430	$O=C$	+1075
$HC-H$	+416				
$C-H$	+335				

The bond enthalpy of $O=O$ is +497 kJ mol^{-1}.

(a)   (i)   Calculate the mean bond enthalpies in methane, water and
             carbon dioxide.   [1]
       (ii) Hence calculate the enthalpy change of combustion of
             methane (CH_4) forming carbon dioxide and steam.   [4]

(b)   Carbon burns in an incomplete supply of oxygen to form carbon monoxide.
       The standard enthalpy change of atomisation ΔH_a is the enthalpy change
       when a substance, in its standard state, decomposes to form 1 mole of
       atoms in the gaseous state under standard conditions. (For diatomic
       elements it is equal to half the bond enthalpy.)

       The standard enthalpy change of formation of carbon monoxide
       is −111 kJ mol^{-1}.

       ΔH_a for carbon is +715 kJ mol^{-1} and ΔH_a for oxygen is +249 kJ mol^{-1}.

       (i)   From this information show that the bond enthalpy in carbon
             monoxide is +1075 kJ mol^{-1}.   [3]

       (ii) Suggest why the 'second bond' enthalpy for carbon dioxide and the
             bond enthalpy for carbon monoxide are the same.   [1]

(c)   The standard enthalpy changes of combustion for three alcohols are:

       CH_3OH −726 kJ mol^{-1} C_2H_5OH −1366 kJ mol^{-1} C_3H_7OH −2017 kJ mol^{-1}

       Using these figures:

       (i)   predict, with a reason, the standard enthalpy change of
             combustion of C_4H_9OH.   [2]

       (ii) predict, with a reason, the standard enthalpy change of
             combustion of water and comment on your answer.   [2]

Answers

(1) (a)   **A:** + ve
B: is the enthalpy change that accompanies the neutralisation of an acid by a base to form 1 mole of $H_2O(l)$ under standard conditions.
C: is the enthalpy change that takes place when one mole of a substance reacts completely with oxygen under standard conditions, all reactants and products being in their standard state
D: −ve   **E:** is the standard enthalpy change of formation .

Examiner's tip

Note that the definitions refer to 1 mole.

(b)   −602 kJ mol^{-1}. The enthalpy of formation is for the formation of 1 mole of magnesium oxide.

Examiner's tip

Do not forget the sign + or −, and the units. Enthalpy of reaction must always be quoted with an equation to show the molar amounts that are reacting.

(c)   The physical state at a pressure of 100 kPa and at a stated temperature (normally 298 K).

(d)(i) The acids and alkalis are fully ionised.
The enthalpy of neutralisation is for the formation of 1 mole of water. The reaction taking place in each case is: $H^+(aq) + OH^-(aq) \rightarrow H_2O(l)$.

Examiner's tip

Strong acids and strong alkalis ionise completely.

(ii) The value for a weak acid and a strong alkali is less exothermic because energy has to be used to ionise the weak acid.

(2) (a)(i) methane $+411.5$ kJ mol^{-1}; water $+462$ kJ mol^{-1}; carbon dioxide $+803$ kJ mol^{-1}.

(ii) Equation is $CH_4(g) + 2O_2(g) \rightarrow CO_2(g) + 2H_2O(g)$.

Energy required to break bonds $= 4 \times 411.5$ (from CH_4) $+ 2 \times 497$ from oxygen
$= +2640$ kJ
Energy released by bond making $= (2 \times 803)$ (from carbon dioxide) $+ 4 \times 462$
(from water) $= 3454$ kJ
$\Delta H_c = -814$ kJ mol^{-1}

Examiner's tip

Bond breaking is endothermic; bond making is exothermic. All combustion reactions are exothermic.

(b)(i) $C(s) + \frac{1}{2}O_2(g) \rightarrow CO(g)$ $\Delta H_f = -111$ kJ mol^{-1}
$C(s) \rightarrow C(g)$ $\Delta H_a = +715$ kJ mol^{-1}
$\frac{1}{2}O_2(g) \rightarrow O$ $\Delta H_a = +249$ kJ mol^{-1}
$CO(g) \rightarrow C(g) + O(g)$ $\Delta H = -(-111) + 715 + 249 = 1075$ kJ mol^{-1}
Bond enthalpy $= +1075$ kJ mol^{-1} (working two marks; answer 1 mark)

(ii) The same bonds are being broken.

Examiner's tip

When the first C=O bond is broken in carbon dioxide, the structure changes to the bonding in carbon monoxide.

(c)(i) Differences in ΔH_c are 640 kJ mol^{-1} and 651 kJ mol^{-1} so value for C_4H_9OH is between -2650 and -2680 kJ mol^{-1}.

(ii) ΔH_c will be between -80 and -90 kJ mol^{-1} but would expect it to be zero.

Examiner's tip

If a CH_2 is subtracted from CH_3OH we get water. Water can be considered as an alcohol without carbon.

Questions with model answers

C grade candidate – mark scored 5/10

See Revise AS
Study Guide 6.1

Examiner's Commentary

When excess lumps of barium carbonate are added to dilute hydrochloric acid the following reaction takes place:

$$BaCO_3(s) + 2HCl(aq) \rightarrow BaCl_2(aq) + H_2O(l) + CO_2(g)$$

Two experiments were carried out to follow the rate of this reaction. The results were plotted

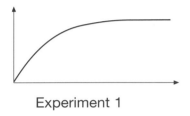

Experiment 1

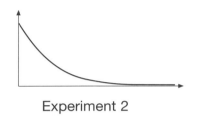

Experiment 2

(a) What would have been plotted on the y-axis in **(i)** Experiment 1 and **(ii)** Experiment 2? [2]

(i) The mass of reactants. (ii) The volume of carbon dioxide ✔ ✗.

> You have identified them the wrong way round, hence 1 mark.

(b) State **three** ways in which the rate of this reaction could be increased. [3]

By using smaller lumps of barium carbonate ✔ heating the acid ✔ and increasing the concentration of the acid ✔.

> Catalysts speed up reactions but there is no catalyst for this reaction.

(c) If dilute sulphuric acid had been used instead of hydrochloric acid, the reaction stops almost immediately. Suggest a reason for this observation. [2]

Sulphuric acid is a weak acid ✗ ✗.

> Barium sulphate would be formed, which is insoluble in water and would prevent any further reaction from taking place.

(d) State, with reasons, whether the total volume of carbon dioxide given off would increase, decrease or stay the same if: [2]

(i) more lumps of barium carbonate were used?

It would stay the same – barium carbonate is in excess ✔.

(ii) the experiments were performed at a higher temperature?

There would be more – temperature speeds up the rate of reaction ✗.

> Although the same number of moles of CO_2 is formed, you must remember that gases expand when they are heated.

(e) The total volume of carbon dioxide given off is slightly less than the theoretical value. What can you deduce from this observation? [1]

The reaction finished early ✗.

> Carbon dioxide is slightly soluble in water.

A grade candidate – mark scored 8/10

 See Revise AS Study Guide 6.1 and 6.2

The graph below shows the Boltzmann distribution curve for the same amount of a gas sample at two different temperatures.

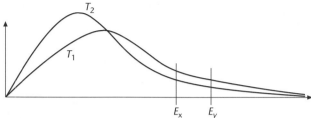

Examiner's Commentary

(a) **(i)** What is the label for the y-axis? **[2]**

Number of molecules ✔ ✗

You should have added 'with a given energy'.

(ii) Is T_1 greater or less than T_2? Give a reason for your answer. **[1]**

Greater than. There are a greater number of molecules with higher energy. ✔

The number of particles is the same, but they are distributed differently.

(iii) What do E_x and E_y represent? **[2]**

E_x = *activation energy with a catalyst* ✔.
E_y = *activation energy for the reaction* ✔.

(b) Explain, in terms of the collision theory, why an increase in temperature increases the rate of a chemical reaction. **[2]**

It brings about more collisions each second ✔ *and a greater proportion of the molecules exceed the activation energy* ✔.

Notice that an increase in energy has two effects. A rise of 10°C approximately doubles the rate of a reaction.

(c) The gas, nitrogen monoxide, NO, was used as a catalyst in the manufacture of sulphur trioxide. **[3]**

$$2SO_2(g) + O_2(g) \rightleftharpoons 2SO_3(g)$$

(i) Why is nitrogen monoxide a homogeneous catalyst for this reaction?

It is in the same physical state as the reactants and products. ✔

(ii) Nitrogen monoxide provides an alternative route for the reaction. It causes the reaction to take place in two stages. The second stage is

$$2SO_2(g) + 2NO_2(g) \rightarrow 2SO_3(g) + 2NO(g)$$

Write an equation for the first stage.

$2SO_2(g) + 2NO(g) \rightarrow 2SO_3 + N_2(g)$ ✗

The second-stage equation tells you that NO_2 has been formed and the overall equation tells you that oxygen is involved. The first stage should be $2NO(g) + O_2(g) \rightarrow 2NO_2(g)$. The first and second stages added together give the overall reaction.

(iii) How does the catalyst, nitrogen monoxide, speed up the rate of the reaction?

It lowers the activation energy. ✔

Exam practice questions

Answers on p. 36

(1) The following results were obtained when manganese(IV) oxide, MnO_2, was added to 50 cm^3 of hydrogen peroxide solution. Hydrogen peroxide decomposes very slowly into oxygen and water at room temperature.

	lumps of MnO_2	powdered MnO_2
Volume of hydrogen peroxide used	50 cm^3	50 cm^3
Temperature of hydrogen peroxide	25°C	25°C
Mass at start	1.50 g	1.00 g
Mass at finish	1.50 g	1.00 g
Appearance at finish	powder	powder
Time to give off 25 cm^3 of oxygen	15 seconds	10 seconds

(a) Use these results to define a catalyst.   [2]

(b) The decomposition of hydrogen peroxide into water and oxygen can be catalysed by adding OH$^-$ ions. How would you show that OH$^-$ ions were not used up in this reaction?   [3]

(c) Explain why a catalyst increases the rate of a chemical reaction.   [2]

(d) Write an equation to show that concentrated hydrogen peroxide is both a weak acid and a dibasic (diprotic) acid.   [2]

(2)   A dynamic homogeneous equilibrium is established when hydrogen
and iodine react as shown

$$H_2(g) + I_2(g) \rightleftharpoons 2HI(g)$$

(a)   Use this equation to explain what is meant by   **[3]**

   (i) *homogeneous*

   (ii) *equilibrium*?

(b)   A mixture of the same number of moles of hydrogen and iodine was put in
a container and then placed in an oven at 425°C. The graph below shows
the concentrations of hydrogen, iodine and hydrogen iodide over a
period of 1 minute. (Time zero is when the gases had reached a
temperature of 425°C.)

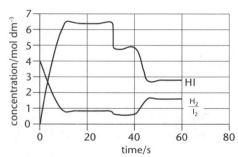

   (i) Why are the molar concentrations of iodine and hydrogen
the same throughout this experiment?   **[1]**

   (ii) Estimate how many seconds the reaction takes to reach equilibrium
for the first time?   **[1]**

   (iii) After how many seconds was some hydrogen iodide removed from
the container?   **[1]**

   (iv) After 40 seconds the oven was turned up to a much higher
temperature. State with a reason whether the reaction between
hydrogen and iodine is exothermic or endothermic.   **[2]**

(c)   Explain why an increase in pressure has no effect on the position of
this equilibrium.   **[1]**

(d)   Iodine acts as a catalyst for the reaction between benzene and
chlorine. Iodine forms an intermediate compound with chlorine.
Suggest a formula for this compound.   **[1]**

Answers

(1) (a) A catalyst speeds up a chemical reaction but is not used up in the reaction.

(b) By titrating measured volumes with standard acid at the start of the reaction and titrating the same volume with standard acid at the end of the reaction. The two values will be the same.

Examiner's tip

A catalyst is not used up in a chemical reaction. It may change in its appearance. In this example manganese(IV) oxide started as lumps but ended up as a powder.

(c) A catalyst allows a reaction to take place via a different route with a lower activation energy.

Examiner's tip

Since the activation energy is lowered there will be more molecules with sufficient energy to react. Thus the reaction speeds up because there are more effective collisions.

(d) $H_2O_2(aq) \rightleftharpoons 2H^+(aq) + O_2^{2-}(aq)$

(2) (a)(i) All the substances are in the same physical state: in this case, gases.

Examiner's tip

A heterogeneous catalyst is in a different phase from the reactants. In the manufacture of ammonia the catalyst is iron, which is a solid; the reactants, nitrogen and hydrogen, are gases.

(ii) The rate of the forward reaction = the rate of the reverse reaction.

Examiner's tip

At equilibrium, the concentrations remain constant.

(b)(i) Equimolar amounts react.

Examiner's tip

1 mole of H_2 and 1 mole of I_2 give 2 moles of HI.

(ii) 10 seconds
(iii) 30 seconds.

Examiner's tip

The clue was that the amounts of HI, I_2 and H_2 were reduced.

(iv) The reaction between hydrogen and iodine is exothermic since less hydrogen iodide is formed at the higher temperature.

(c) There are an equal number of gaseous molecules on each side of the equation.

Examiner's tip

Note, you must only consider gaseous substances when looking at the effect of pressure.

(d) ICl.

Questions with model answers

C grade candidate – mark scored 7/14

See Revise AS Study Guide 7.4 and 7.6

(a) The compound $C_2H_4Br_2(l)$ can be made by reacting ethene with bromine.

Examiner's Commentary

(i) Write the equation, together with state symbols, for this reaction. **[2]**

$C_2H_4(g) + Br_2(g) \rightarrow C_2H_4Br_2(l)$ ✗ ✔

Bromine is a liquid $Br_2(l)$.

(ii) What are the conditions for this reaction to take place? **[1]**

It requires sunlight ✗.

The reaction takes place at room temperature – you are confusing this with the alkane reaction.

(iii) What colour change would you see in this reaction? **[2]**

The bromine is decolourised ✔ ✗.

You must give the colour change – orange to colourless.

(b) $C_2H_4Br_2$ can also be made by reacting ethane with bromine. Unfortunately, this method of preparation forms a mixture of bromoalkanes. Suggest the molecular formula of another bromoalkane product of this reaction. **[1]**

$C_2H_3Br_3$ ✔

Many others are possible, e.g. $C_2H_2Br_4$, C_2HBr_5, C_2Br_6.

(c) $C_2H_4Br_2$ can be refluxed with aqueous sodium hydroxide forming an organic product **B** and bromide ions.

(i) Suggest the formula of the organic product **B**. **[1]**

$C_2H_4(OH)_2$ ✔

(ii) Describe how would you show that bromide ions had been formed? **[3]**

Add silver nitrate ✔, *a cream precipitate of silver bromide is formed* ✔ ✗.

You must first add excess nitric acid to remove the sodium hydroxide that would give a precipitate with silver nitrate.

(d) Briefly describe how ethene can be converted into ethanol using sulphuric acid. **[2]**

Pass ethene into concentrated sulphuric acid ✗ ✗.

Nothing happens in the cold. To convert ethene to ethanol, we need steam and concentrated sulphuric acid.

(e) Suggest how ethene can be obtained from ethanol. **[2]**

Use heat ✔ *with a dehydrating agent* ✗.

You should name the dehydrating agent – excess concentrated sulphuric acid.

Questions with model answers

? *See Revise AS Study Guide 7.5*

A grade candidate – mark scored 8/10

Ethanoic acid and glucose (molecular formula $C_6H_{12}O_6$) have the same empirical formula.

Examiner's Commentary

(a) What is the structural formula of ethanoic acid? **[1]**

CH_3COOH ✔.

Don't forget to include the C in the COOH group when naming acids.

(b) Show that ethanoic acid and glucose have the same empirical formula. **[2]**

Molecular formula of ethanoic acid is $C_2H_4O_2$, simplest formula is CH_2O ✔.

Simplest formula for glucose is CH_2O, so they both have the same empirical formula. ✔.

(c) Suggest the product formed when glucose is dehydrated by concentrated sulphuric acid. **[1]**

Carbon ✔.

Six molecules of water would be removed leaving 6C.

(d) Ethanoic acid can be formed from ethanol.

$C_2H_5OH(l) + 2[O] \rightarrow CH_3COOH(l) + H_2O(l)$

(i) State suitable reagents for this reaction and the essential conditions required: **[3]**

$Cr_2O_7^{2-}$ ✗ and H_2SO_4 ✔ reflux ✔.

You must give the name or formula of the reagents. $Cr_2O_7^{2-}$ is NOT the name or the correct formula of the reagent. Potassium dichromate (VI) ($K_2Cr_2O_7$) is a suitable reagent.

(ii) State, with reasons, whether or not the formation of ethanoic acid from ethanol is an example of the following types of reaction: **[3]**

Type of reaction	Reason
Addition	*no, two products are formed, not one* ✔
Oxidation	*yes, oxygen is added* ✔
Hydrolysis	*yes, water is formed* ✗

No, hydrolysis is a reaction with water – in this case water is formed.

Exam practice questions

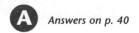 *Answers on p. 40*

(1) An alcohol has a relative molecular mass of 74 and has the following composition by mass: C, 64.9%; H, 13.5%; O, 21.6%.

(a) Calculate the empirical formula of the alcohol and show that its molecular formula is the same as the empirical formula. **[4]**

(b) Draw the displayed formula of the **four** possible isomers of this alcohol. **[4]**

(c) Compound **F**, one of these isomers, can be oxidised to form a ketone, **G.** **[2]**

    (i) Show the structure of compound **G.**

    (ii) Deduce which of the four alcohols in **(b)** is compound **F.**

(2) **X** is an unsaturated hydrocarbon of relative molecular mass 54. **X** does not have any triple bonds. **X** melts at −109°C and boils at −5°C.

(a) Will **X** be a solid, liquid or gas at room temperature and pressure? Give a reason for your answer. **[1]**

(b) How would you show that **X** was unsaturated? **[2]**

(c) At room temperature and pressure, 2.7 g of **X** reacts with 2.4 dm^3 of hydrogen. Show that each molecule of **X** contains two double bonds. **[2]**

(d) Show that the molecular formula of **X** is C_4H_6. **[1]**

(e) What is the empirical formula of **X**? **[1]**

(f) **Y** is an unsaturated hydrocarbon with the molecular formula C_4H_8. Draw possible structures of **two** structural isomers of **Y**. **[2]**

(g) If you were given a mixture of these two isomers of **Y**, suggest how would you separate them. **[1]**

(h) Draw the skeletal structure of one of these isomers of **Y**. **[1]**

Answers

(1) (a)

C:
$$\frac{64.9}{12}$$

H:
$$\frac{13.5}{1}$$

O:
$$\frac{21.6}{16}$$

$$= 5.41 : 13.5 : 1.35$$

Dividing each by 1.35 gives 4 : 10 : 1

Empirical formula is $C_4H_{10}O$, which has a mass of 74 which is the M_r of the molecule. Therefore molecular formula is the same as the empirical formula.

(b)

H–C–C–C–C–O–H (with H atoms on each carbon)

H–C–C–C–H (with O–H above middle carbon, and H–C–H branch)

H–C–C–C–O–H (with H–C–H branch)

H–C–C–C–C–H (with O–H above third carbon, H above)

Examiner's tip

Displayed means showing all atoms and bonds.

(c)(i)

H–C–C–C–C–H (with O double bonded to third carbon)

(ii)

H–C–C–C–C–H (with O–H group, H above)

(2) (a)   **X** will be a gas as its m.p. and b.p. are both below room temperature.

(b)   Add bromine/bromine water; it changes from orange to colourless.

(c)   2.7g of X reacts with 2.4 dm³ of hydrogen therefore 54g reacts with 48 dm³, which is 2 moles of hydrogen, therefore it has 2 double bonds.

Examiner's tip

One mole of hydrogen is required to saturate one double bond.

(d) $4 \times 12 + 6 \times 1 = 54$.

(e) C_2H_3.

(f)   Any two from

$$\begin{array}{c} H \\ H \end{array} C=C \begin{array}{c} CH_3 \\ CH_3 \end{array} \quad \begin{array}{c} H \\ H \end{array} C=C \begin{array}{c} H \\ CH_2-CH_3 \end{array} \quad \begin{array}{c} H_3C \\ H \end{array} C=C \begin{array}{c} CH_3 \\ H \end{array} \text{ or } \begin{array}{c} H_3C \\ H \end{array} C=C \begin{array}{c} H \\ CH_3 \end{array}$$

(g)   Liquefy and then fractional distillation.

Examiner's tip

Isomers have different boiling points, and therefore can be separated by this method.

(h)   one from

Questions with model answers

C grade candidate – mark scored 6/10

 See Revise A2 Study Guide 2.3 and 2.4

Examiner's Commentary

The data below is for 0.10 molar solutions of various acids at 298 K.

acid	equation	pH	K_a/mol dm^{-3}	pK_a
hydrocyanic acid	$HCN(aq) \rightleftharpoons H^+(aq) + CN^-(aq)$	5.2	4.9×10^{-10}	
	$CH_3COOH(aq) \rightleftharpoons H^+(aq)$ $+ CH_3COO^-(aq)$	2.9	1.7×10^{-5}	4.8
hydrofluoric acid		2.1	5.6×10^{-4}	3.3
phosphoric(V) acid	$H_3PO_4(aq) \rightleftharpoons H^+(aq)$ $+ H_2PO_4^-(aq)$		7.9×10^{-3}	1.8

(a) Define K_a and pK_a for a weak acid HA. **[2]**

$$K_a = \frac{[H^+(aq)][A^-(aq)]}{[HA(aq)]}$$ ✔

$$pK_a = -log_{10}K_a$$ ✔

(b) **(i)** Name the acid with a pH of 2.9. **[2]**

Ethanoic acid ✔.

(ii) Which of the four acids is the weakest acid?

Hydrocyanic acid ✔.

The weakest acid has the smallest K_a value.

(c) Phenolphthalein is colourless at pH 8.2 and deep pink at pH 10. Which of the above acids could be titrated against 0.1 M sodium hydroxide using phenolphthalein as indicator? **[1]**

All except hydrocyanic acid ✘.

Phenolphthalein can be used to titrate a weak acid or a strong acid against sodium hydroxide (strong alkali). So, all 4 acids could be titrated against it.

(d) **(i)** Write the equation for the ionisation of hydrofluoric acid. **[5]**

$HF(aq) \rightleftharpoons H^+(aq) + F^-(aq)$ ✔

(ii) Calculate pK_a for hydrocyanic acid.

$pK_a = -log_{10}[4.9 \times 10^{-10}]$ ✔ $= -9.3$ ✘

You forgot to change the sign; minus times a minus gives a plus.

(iii) Calculate the pH of phosphoric(V) acid.

1.8 ✘*, the same as the pK_a* ✘.

$[H^+] = [H_2PO_4^{2-}]$
$7.9 \times 10^{-3} = [H^+]^2/0.1$
$[H^+] = \sqrt{7.9 \times 10^{-4}}$
$= 0.0281$
$pH = -log_{10}[0.0281]$
$= 1.6$

Questions with model answers

A grade candidate – mark scored 9/10

 See Revise A2 Study Guide 2.1 and 2.2

Examiner's Commentary

The following two equations represent the reaction between hydrogen and iodine to form hydrogen iodide.

$$H_2(g) + I_2(g) \rightleftharpoons 2HI(g) \qquad \text{equilibrium constant} = K_1$$

$$\tfrac{1}{2}H_2(g) + \tfrac{1}{2}I_2(g) \rightleftharpoons HI(g) \qquad \text{equilibrium constant} = K_2$$

(a) **(i)** Give the expressions for K_1 and K_2. **[2]**

$$K_1 = \frac{[HI]^2}{[H_2][I_2]} \quad ✔ \qquad K_2 = \frac{[HI]}{\sqrt{[H_2]}\sqrt{[I_2]}} \quad ✔$$

(ii) What is the relationship between K_1 and K_2? **[1]**

$$K_1 = K_2^2 \quad ✔$$

You could have solved this by looking at your answer to (a)(i).

(b) An equilibrium mixture for the above reaction contains 6.4 mol dm^{-3} of hydrogen iodide, 0.8 mol dm^{-3} of hydrogen and 0.8 mol dm^3 of iodine. **[3]**
Calculate **(i)** K_1 **(ii)** K_2.

(i) $K_1 = \dfrac{6.4^2}{0.8 \times 0.8} = 64 \, dm^3 \, mol^{-1}$ ✔ ✗

(ii) $K_2 = \sqrt{64} = 8 \, dm^3 \, mol^{-1}$ ✔

There should be NO units in answers to (b)(i) and (ii).

(c) Under what conditions: **[4]**

(i) does an equilibrium constant K_c have no units?

When there are an equal number of moles that are either (g) or (aq) on both sides ✔.

(ii) is the equilibrium unaffected by pressure?

When there are equal numbers of gaseous molecules on each side ✔.

(iii) is the value for $K_p = K_c$?

When there are equal numbers of gaseous molecules on each side ✔.

(iv) is the same equilibrium position reached in less time?

When a catalyst is added ✔.

When a catalyst is added. A catalyst speeds up the rate of equilibrium, but does not alter the position of the equilibrium.

Exam practice questions

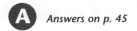 *Answers on p. 45*

(1) The Haber process manufactures ammonia.

$N_2(g) + 3H_2(g) \rightleftharpoons 2NH_3(g)$

During the process 46 kJ of ammonia is given out per mole of ammonia formed.

(a) **(i)** If 1.02×10^6 kg of ammonia are produced per day, calculate how much heat energy is given out each day. **[2]**

(ii) Suggest a use for this heat energy. **[1]**

(b) State Le Chatelier's principle. **[2]**

(c) State the effect on the ammonia equilibrium position if: **[3]**

   (i) more nitrogen was added

   (ii) the mixture was heated

   (iii) water was added

(d) **(i)** Write an expression for K_c and K_p for the above equilibrium. **[2]**

An equilibrium mixture in a sealed 2 dm³ container at 700 K and a pressure of 200 kPa contains 0.6 mol of nitrogen, 2.0 mol of hydrogen and 0.6 mol of ammonia.

   (ii) Calculate the equilibrium concentrations and hence the value, including units, of K_c. **[2]**

   (iii) Calculate the equilibrium partial pressures and hence the value, including units, of K_p. **[3]**

43

Exam practice questions

(2) (a) Using aqueous ethanoic acid (CH_3COOH) as your example, explain what is meant by:

      (i) *dilute acid*   **(ii)** *weak acid*   **(iii)** *monobasic acid*   **[3]**

(b) Calculate the pH of: **[4]**

      (i) 0.20 M sodium hydroxide

      (ii) 0.10 M ethanoic acid ($K_a = 1.7 \times 10^{-5}$ mol dm^{-3}).

(c) Copy and complete the graph below showing the addition of 50 cm^3 of 0.10 M sodium hydroxide to 25 cm^3 of 0.1 M ethanoic acid.   **[2]**

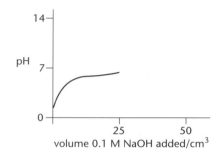

(d) Thymol blue is an indicator. Its various colour changes at different pH values are:

pH	1.2	2.8	9.6
colour	red	yellow	blue

Describe the colour changes when the reaction in **(c)** is performed.   **[2]**

Answers

(1) (a)(i) Moles of ammonia $= \dfrac{1.02 \times 10^9}{17} = 6.0 \times 10^7$ Energy given out $= 2.76 \times 10^9$ kJ

Examiner's tip

The amount was given in kg, which needs converting to grams before you can work out the number of moles.

    (ii) To heat the hydrogen and nitrogen before passing over the iron.

(b) When a constraint is added to a system in equilibrium the equilibrium shifts to ease that constraint.

(c)(i) More ammonia would be produced.
  (ii) Less ammonia would be produced.
 (iii) More ammonia would be formed (ammonia is soluble in water).

(d)(i) $K_c = \dfrac{[NH_3]^2}{[N_2][H_2]^3}$ $K_p = \dfrac{p_{NH_3}^2}{p_{N_2} \times p_{H_2}^3}$

  (ii) $K_c = \dfrac{0.3^2}{0.3 \times 1^3} = 0.3 \, dm^6 mol^{-2}$

Examiner's tip

Since the container was 2 dm^3, the number of moles must be divided by 2 to get the molar concentrations.

  (iii) Total number of moles $= 0.6 + 2.0 + 0.6 = 3.2$ moles.

$p_{N_2} = \dfrac{0.6 \times 200}{3.2} = 37.5 \, kPa$ $p_{H_2} = \dfrac{2 \times 200}{3.2} = 125 \, kPa$ $p_{NH_3} = \dfrac{0.6 \times 200}{3.2} = 37.5 \, kPa$

$K_p = \dfrac{37.5^2}{37.5 \times 125^3} = 1.92 \times 10^{-5} \, kPa^{-2}$

(2) (a)(i) *dilute* – low concentration of ethanoic acid in water
  (ii) *weak* – only partially ionises in water
 (iii) *monobasic* – contains only one proton that can be replaced by a metal ion

(b)(i) $K_w = [H^+][OH^-]$ $[H^+] = \dfrac{1 \times 10^{-14}}{0.2} = 5 \times 10^{-14} \, mol \, dm^{-3}$ pH $= 13.3$

  (ii) $K_a = \dfrac{[CH_3COO^-][H^+]}{[CH_3COOH]} = \dfrac{[H^+]^2}{0.1} = 1.7 \times 10^{-5}$

        $[H^+] = \sqrt{0.1 \times 1.7 \times 10^{-5}} = 1.30 \times 10^{-3}$ pH $= 2.9$

(c) ends at pH $= 13$ a sharp rise at 25 cm^3

(d) It turns from yellow to green (at end point) and finally to blue.

Questions with model answers

See Revise A2
Study Guide 1.1
and 1.2

C grade candidate – mark scored 6/10

Hydrogen and nitrogen(II) oxide (NO) react at 1000 K to form water vapour and nitrogen.

$$2H_2(g) + 2NO(g) \rightarrow 2H_2O(g) + N_2(g)$$

The initial rate was measured for various concentrations of hydrogen and nitrogen(II) oxide.

Initial concentration /mol dm^{-3}		Initial rate of reaction / mol dm^{-3} s^{-1}
H$_2$(g)	NO(g)	
1.0	5.0	2.0
2.0	5.0	4.0
3.0	5.0	6.0
5.0	1.0	0.4
5.0	2.0	1.6
5.0	3.0	3.6

(a) What is the order of reaction with respect to: **(i)** hydrogen **(ii)** nitrogen(II) oxide? **[2]**

(i) first order ✔   *(ii) second order* ✔

Look at the rates and concentrations – if the rate doubles when the concentration doubles, it is first order. If the rate 'squares', it is second order.

(b) Write the rate equation for this reaction. **[1]**

Rate = k[H$_2$]^1 [NO]^2 ✔

(c) Calculate the rate constant under the conditions of this experiment. **[2]**

0.40 ✗ ✗

You forgot to divide by [NO]^2 and you have left out the units. The answer is 0.08 dm^6 mol^{-2} s^{-1}.

(d) Calculate the initial rate of reaction if 5.0 mol dm^{-3} of NO$_2$(g) were added to 5.0 mol dm^{-3} of H$_2$(g). **[2]**

0.40 × 5 × 5^2 = 50 ✔ ✗

Again, you have left out the units. The answer using the correct rate constant is 10 mol dm^{-3} s^{-1}.

(e) Suggest a possible mechanism for this reaction. **[3]**

2NO(g) + H$_2$(g) → 2NOH(g)   fast ✔

2NOH(g) + H$_2$(g) → 2H$_2$O(g) + N$_2$ ✔ *slow* ✗

Although wrong, it is a good suggestion and gets two marks. A likely mechanism is 2NO(g) + H$_2$(g) → H$_2$O$_2$(l) + N$_2$(g) (slow) H$_2$O$_2$(g) + H$_2$(g) → 2H$_2$O (g) (fast) Examiners will accept any sensible mechanism. (Note there are 3 marks for this question but 4 scoring points.)

A grade candidate – mark scored 9/12

*See Revise A2
Study Guide 3.2
and 3.3*

The following are standard electrode potentials for some metal systems

Half reaction	$E^{\ominus}/V$
$Zn^{2+}(aq) + 2e^- \rightleftharpoons Zn(s)$	-0.76
$Fe^{2+}(aq) + 2e^- \rightleftharpoons Fe(s)$	-0.44
$Sn^{2+}(aq) + 2e^- \rightleftharpoons Sn(s)$	-0.14
$Cu^{2+}(aq) + 2e^- \rightleftharpoons Cu(s)$	$+0.34$

Examiner's Commentary

These values give the order of reactivity. The more negative the value, the more reactive the metal.

(a) On what standard half-equation are these $E^{\ominus}$ values based? **[1]**

$2H^+(aq) + 2e^- \rightleftharpoons H_2(g)$ ✔

The standard hydrogen electrode potential of hydrogen is 0.00 volts.

(b) What is the strongest oxidising agent in the above list? **[1]**

Cu ✗.

Should have been $Cu^{2+}(aq)$. The oxidising agents are on the left hand side of the equations. The strongest oxidising agent has the most positive value.

(c) A Daniell cell was used to produce electricity in a home to operate simple electrical devices such as a door bell. It is made up of zinc in zinc sulphate solution and copper in copper(II) sulphate solution. **[5]**

(i) Assuming both solutions are molar, what voltage could this cell produce?

$0.34 - (-0.76) = 1.1$ ✔ $volts$ ✔.

(ii) Write an ionic equation for the reaction taking place.

$Cu^{2+}(aq) + Zn(s) \rightarrow Zn^{2+}(s) + Cu(aq)$ ✔

(iii) Suggest a reason for having a large piece of zinc and keeping solid copper(II) sulphate in the copper(II) sulphate solution.

Zinc reacts and therefore gets used up, the large piece makes it last longer ✔. *Copper gets used up, the solid copper(II) sulphate dissolves, keeping the solution concentrated* ✗.

It is the copper ions in the copper(II) sulphate that get used up.

(c) Both zinc and tin are used effectively to coat iron to prevent it from rusting. Once the coating is scratched, oxygen and water containing dissolved ions come into contact with the coating metal and iron. **[5]**

(i) State, with reasons, whether tin or zinc is best able to prevent iron from rusting under these conditions.

Zinc is more reactive than iron ✔ *– hence loses electrons to Fe^{2+}* ✔ *(sacrificial protection). Tin is less reactive* ✔*, iron loses electrons to tin and therefore rusts more* ✔.

(ii) What is the electrolyte in rusting?

water ✗.

In fact, it is the presence of ions such as HCO_3^- and H^+ formed when carbon dioxide dissolves in water.

Exam practice questions

Answers on p. 50

(1) **(a)** Define the term *standard electrode (redox) potential.* **[4]**

(b) The diagram below shows a hydrogen electrode connected to a copper ion/copper electrode using a salt bridge. The standard electrode potential was found to be + 0.34 volts. **[10]**

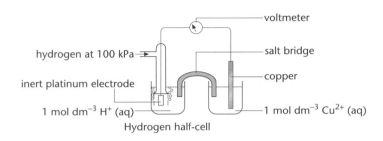

(i) Name a copper salt suitable for use in the Cu^{2+}/Cu electrode. What is the concentration, in mol dm^{-3}, of this solution?

(ii) What concentration, in mol dm^{-3}, of nitric acid (HNO_3) would be needed in the H^+/H_2 electrode?

(iii) Why is a salt bridge used?

(iv) Why does the hydrogen electrode have a platinum electrode?

(v) State, with a reason, the direction of the flow of electrons.

(vi) What would be the Standard Cell Potential of the cell if the volume of the copper salt solution used were doubled?

(c) The standard electrode potential of Cr^{3+}(aq)/Cr(s) is −0.77 volts. Write this statement as a half equation. **[1]**

(d) **(i)** What would be the initial voltage of a standard cell made from a Cu^{2+}(aq)/Cu(s) electrode and a Cr^{3+}(aq)/Cr(s) electrode? **[1]**

(ii) Why would the voltage drop as the cell was used? **[1]**

(2) The acid hydrolysis of methyl ethanoate CH_3COOCH_3 is a first order reaction. The hydrolysis is catalysed by H^+ ions.

$CH_3COOCH_3(aq) + H_2O(l) \rightleftharpoons CH_3COOH(aq) + CH_3OH(aq)$

The following data were obtained in an experiment, carried out at 40°C, to determine the rate constant for the reaction:

Time/min	0	20	40	60	80	100
concentration of CH_3COOCH_3 /mol dm^{-3}	1.00	0.67	0.45	0.30	0.21	0.14
rate/mol dm^{-3} min^{-1}		0.020	0.013	0.009	0.006	0.004	0.003

(a) (i) Write the rate equation for this reaction. **[1]**

(ii) Calculate the rate constant, including units, for this reaction. **[2]**

(b) (i) Why are the units of rate mol dm^{-3} min^{-1}? **[1]**

(ii) Explain why the rate of reaction slows down as the reaction proceeds. **[1]**

(iii) Explain why the rate of reaction increases using higher temperatures. **[2]**

(c) (i) Plot a graph of concentration of CH_3COOCH_3 against time. **[6]**

(ii) Use the graph to determine the concentration of CH_3COOCH_3 after 2 hours.

(iii) How does the half-life from this graph show that the reaction is first order with respect to CH_3COOCH_3?

Answers

(1) (a) Standard conditions are 298 K with solution concentrations of 1 mol dm^{-3} and a gas pressure of 100 kPa. The standard electrode potential is the e.m.f. of a standard half-cell compared with a standard hydrogen half-cell.

(b)(i) Copper(II) sulphate/nitrate 1 mol dm^{-3}.　　**(ii)** 1 mol dm^{-3}.

(iii) A salt bridge allows ions in the two electrolytes to migrate from one half-cell to another without the electrolytes themselves mixing.

> **Examiner's tip**
>
> *The salt in the salt bridge must not interfere with the reaction taking place.*

(iv) It is impossible to connect wire to hydrogen gas, you need a metal that does not react with acid.

(v) From hydrogen to copper. Hydrogen loses electrons more readily than copper.

(vi) No effect.

> **Examiner's tip**
>
> *Electrode potential does not depend on the amounts of reactants and products but it does depend on concentrations.*

(c) $Cr^{3+}(aq) + 3e^- \rightleftharpoons Cr(s)$　　$E^{\ominus} = -0.77$ volts

(d)(i) 1.11 volts

(ii) Concentration of copper salt will reduce as copper is deposited on the electrode.

(2) (a)(i) Rate $= k[CH_3COOCH_3]^1$

(ii) $0.02 = k[1]$　　$k = 0.02$ min^{-1}

(b)(i) Rate of change of concentration (mol dm^{-3}) with time (min^{-1}).

(ii) The concentration of methyl ethanoate decreases as the reaction proceeds.

(iii) There are more collisions, more particles with energy greater than the activation energy .

(c)(i)

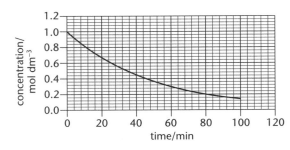

(axis correct
plotting of points correct
smooth line)

> **Examiner's tip**
>
> *Time must be on the x-axis.*

(ii) 0.09 – 0.11 mol dm^{-3}.

(iii) Half-life constant at 34–36 min at least two readings taken.

Questions with model answers

C grade candidate – mark scored 6/10

See Revise A2
Study Guide 3.1

The Born–Haber cycle below represents enthalpy changes when a Group 2 metal (Mg, Ca, Sr) reacts with a Group 7 non-metal (Cl, Br, I) to form a metal halide.

Examiner's Commentary

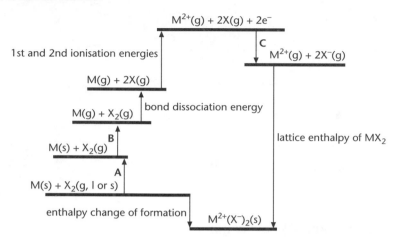

$M^{2+}(g) + 2X(g) + 2e^-$

1st and 2nd ionisation energies

$M(g) + 2X(g)$

C

$M^{2+}(g) + 2X^-(g)$

bond dissociation energy

$M(g) + X_2(g)$

B

$M(s) + X_2(g)$

A

$M(s) + X_2(g, l$ or $s)$

lattice enthalpy of MX_2

enthalpy change of formation

$M^{2+}(X^-)_2(s)$

(a) For which halogen(s) Cl, Br, I, will the value of the enthalpy change **A** be zero? **[1]**

Chlorine, its a gas already ✔.

(b) (i) Name the enthalpy change **B**. **[1]**

Standard enthalpy of atomisation ✔.

(ii) State, with reasons, which of the Group 2 metals, Mg, Ca, Sr, will have the smallest value for **B**. **[2]**

Strontium ✔, *the metallic bond gets weaker going down a group* ✔.

(c) (i) Name the enthalpy change **C**. **[1]**

(Twice) electron affinity ✔.

(ii) State, with reasons, which of the halogens Cl, Br, I, will have the largest numerical value for **C**? **[2]**

Chlorine ✔ *it has the lowest atomic number of these three halogens* ✗.

Although true, it does not answer the question. Because chlorine has the smallest atom of the three, it will attract electrons most strongly.

(d) (i) Name **two** factors that affect the size of the lattice enthalpy. **[2]**

Ionisation energy ✗ *and formula of compound* ✗.

*It is size **and** charge on the ions.*

(ii) Which Group 2 halide will have the most exothermic lattice energy? **[1]**

Strontium iodide ✗.

Using the information above, it will be magnesium chloride.

Questions with model answers

A grade candidate – mark scored 6/8

? *See Revise A2 Study Guide 4.1*

The table below gives data on oxides in Period 3 of the Periodic Table.

Element	Na	Mg	Al	Si	P	S	Cl
Formula of oxide	Na_2O	MgO	Al_2O_3	SiO_2	P_4O_{10} P_4O_6	SO_3 SO_2	Cl_2O_7 Cl_2O
ΔH_f per mole of oxygen (O_2) used /kJ mol^{-1}	−832	−602	−1117	−910	−597 −547	−263 −297	+76 +161

Examiner's Commentary

(a) What is the oxidation number of chlorine in **(i)** Cl_2O_7 **(ii)** Cl_2O? **[1]**

(i) +7   (ii) +1 ✔.

O.N. of oxygen is always −2 except when combined with fluorine or in peroxides.

(b) Divide these oxides into **(i)** ionic bonding **(ii)** covalent bonding. **[2]**

(i) Ionic: Na_2O, MgO, Al_2O_3 ✔.

Al_2O_3 could be either ionic or covalent.

(ii) Covalent: SiO_2, P_4O_{10}, P_4O_6, SO_3, SO_2, Cl_2O_7, Cl_2O ✔.

(c) Explain the difference between the ΔH_f values of SiO_2 and SO_2. **[1]**

SiO_2 has a giant molecular structure, SO_2 has a simple molecular structure ✔.

(d) Using the figures in the table above it can be shown that the enthalpy change of formation of sodium oxide is −416 kJ mol^{-1}.

(i) Write the equation for the formation of 1 mole of aluminium oxide. **[1]**

$2Al(s) + \frac{3}{2} O_2(g) \rightarrow Al_2O_3(s)$ ✔

(ii) Calculate the enthalpy change of formation of aluminium oxide. **[1]**

$\frac{3}{2} \times (-1117) = -1675.5$ kJ mol^{-1} ✔.

(e) State, with a reason, the least stable oxide. **[2]**

Cl_2O_7 ✗ *It has a less exothermic value* ✗.

In general, the less exothermic the enthalpy change of formation, the less stable the compound (Cl_2O).

Exam practice questions

Answers on p. 55

(1) The lattice enthalpy for potassium iodide can be found using a Born–Haber cycle.

(a) Write the equation, including state symbols, for the lattice enthalpy of potassium iodide. **[1]**

(b) **(i)** Use the data below to construct a Born–Haber cycle. **[3]**

Enthalpy change	/kJ mol^{-1}
1st electron affinity of iodine	−314
1st ionisation energy of potassium	+420
Atomisation of iodine $\frac{1}{2}I_2(s) \rightarrow I(g)$	+107
Atomisation of potassium	+90
Formation of potassium iodide	−328

(ii) Show that the experimental lattice enthalpy of potassium iodide is −631 kJ mol^{-1}. **[2]**

(c) Explain the following observations: **[2]**

(i) The theoretical value for the lattice enthalpy of potassium iodide is −631 kJ mol^{-1}.

(ii) For silver iodide, AgI, the experimental value for the lattice enthalpy is −736 kJ mol^{-1} but the theoretical value is −865 kJ mol^{-1}.

(d) The hydration enthalpies for potassium and iodide ions are given by the processes:

$K^+(g) + (aq) \rightarrow K^+(aq)$ $\Delta H = -304$ kJ mol^{-1}
$I^-(g) + (aq) \rightarrow I^-(aq)$ $\Delta H = -306$ kJ mol^{-1}
The lattice enthalpy of potassium iodide is −631 kJ mol^{-1}.
The enthalpy change of solution of potassium iodide is given by:
$KI(s) \rightarrow K^+(aq) + I^-(aq)$

Using this information, calculate the enthalpy change of solution of potassium iodide. **[2]**

(e) Why does potassium iodide dissolve in water but not in tetrachloromethane? **[2]**

Exam practice questions

(2) The table below gives some data about the chlorides of elements in Period 3:

Element	Na	Mg	Al	Si	P	S	Cl
Formula	NaCl	$MgCl_2$	Al_2Cl_6	$SiCl_4$	PCl_3 PCl_5	S_2Cl_2	Cl_2
B.p. /°C	1465	1418	423	57	76 decomposes	136	−34
Does (molten) liquid chloride conduct electricity?	yes, electrolysis takes place	yes, electrolysis takes place	no	no	no	no	no
Action of water	soluble	soluble	reacts	reacts	reacts	reacts	reacts
pH of aqueous solution	7	6	2	2	2	1	1
Electronegativity of element	0.9	1.2	1.5	1.8	2.1	2.5	3.0

(a) What evidence is there that the bonding in the chlorides changes from ionic to covalent across this period? **[2]**

(b) What is formed at the positive electrode (anode) when molten $MgCl_2$ is electrolysed ? **[1]**

(c) What is the difference between electronegativity and electron affinity? **[2]**

(d) By considering ionic size and charge, the boiling point of $MgCl_2$ should be higher than that of NaCl. However $MgCl_2$ has a lower boiling point than sodium chloride. Suggest a reason why the boiling point of $MgCl_2$ is lower than that of NaCl. **[1]**

(e) When PCl_5 is heated it decomposes, forming a liquid, **A** and a gas, **B**. Suggest their identities. **[2]**

Answers

(1) (a) $K^+(g) + I^-(g) \rightarrow KI(s)$

(b)(i)   Potassium part of cycle (90 + 420), iodide part of cycle (107 − 314) KI part of cycle (−328 and lattice energy)

   (ii)   328 + 90 + 107 + 420 = 945; − 945 = −314 + lattice energy = − 631kJ mol^{-1}

(c)(i)   Potassium iodide is an almost 100% ionic compound.
   (ii)   Silver iodide has a proportion of covalent bonding.

(d)   − (− 631) − 304 − 306 = + 21kJ mol^{-1}

(e)   Potassium iodide is an ionic solid, ionic solids dissolve in polar solvents such as water. Tetrachloromethane is non-polar.

(2) (a)   Molten liquids on left of table do conduct electricity but liquids on the right of the table do not conduct. Ions are required for conductivity.

(b)   Chlorine

(c)   Electron affinity is the attraction of an atom for an electron.
   Electronegativity is the relative attraction of an atom for a shared pair of electrons in a bond.

(d)   Magnesium chloride might contain some covalent bonding.

(e)   A: phosphorus trichloride   B: chlorine

Questions with model answers

C grade candidate – mark scored 6/10

See Revise A2 Study Guide 4.3, 4.8 and 3.3

Iron (atomic number 26) reacts with chlorine to form iron(III) chloride and with hydrogen chloride to form iron(II) chloride.

Examiner's Commentary

(a) Explain why iron can form two chlorides. **[3]**

Electronic structure of iron is $[Ar] 4s^2 3d^6$. ✔ It can lose the two 4s electrons to form Fe^{2+} ✔, and for Fe^{3+} it will also lose 1 electron from $3d^6$ to make it stable with 5 half-filled orbitals ✔.

Remember that filled and half-filled orbitals are more stable.

(b) Explain the following observations: **[4]**

(i) anhydrous iron(II) chloride is white but a solution of iron(II) chloride in water is green.

complex ion $[Fe(H_2O)_6]^{2+}$ formed ✔.

(ii) when sodium hydroxide solution is added to iron(II) chloride solution a green precipitate is formed that slowly turns brown.

green precipitate is iron(II) hydroxide ✔ oxidised by the air to brown iron(III) hydroxide ✔.

(iii) an aqueous solution containing $[Fe(H_2O)_6]^{3+}$ ions is weakly acidic.

nitric acid is formed ✗.

The hydrated ion donates protons to water $[Fe(H_2O)_6]^{3+}(aq)$ $+ H_2O(l) \rightleftharpoons$ $[Fe(H_2O)_5(OH)]^{2+}(aq)$ $+ H_3O^+(aq)$.

(c) Use the standard electrode potentials below to explain the difference in the reactions between iron(III) chloride solution and **(i)** potassium bromide, **(ii)** potassium iodide. **[3]**

$$Fe^{3+}(aq) + e^- \rightleftharpoons Fe^{2+}(aq) \quad + 0.77 \text{ volts}$$

$$I_2(aq) + 2e^- \rightleftharpoons 2I^-(aq) \quad + 0.54 \text{ volts}$$

$$Br_2(aq) + 2e^- \rightleftharpoons 2Br^-(aq) \quad + 1.09 \text{ volts}$$

from the electrode potentials ✗ it can be seen that (i) bromine will be formed ✗. (ii) iron(III) iodide will be formed ✗.

The Fe^{3+}/Fe^{2+} system is more negative than the Br_2/Br^-; therefore its reaction will proceed to the left, hence iron(III) chloride will not react with KBr.
The I_2/I^- system is more negative than the Fe^{3+}/Fe^{2+}; therefore its reaction will proceed to the left, hence iodine will be formed and Fe^{2+} ions.

A grade candidate – mark scored 8/10

*See Revise A2
Study Guide 4.4
and 4.6*

(a) When dilute sulphuric acid is added to copper(I) oxide, a pink solid **X** and a blue solution **Y** are formed. The pink solid **X** conducts electricity. **[5]**

Examiner's Commentary

(i) Identify **X** and **Y**.

X is copper ✔ *and Y is an aqueous solution of copper(II) sulphate* ✔.

If a solid conducts electricity it must be a metal. Copper is one of the few coloured metals, gold is another.

(ii) Write an equation for the reaction

$Cu_2O(s) + H_2SO_4(aq) \rightarrow Cu(s) + CuSO_4(aq) + H_2O(l)$ ✔

(iii) Use the reaction to explain the meaning of disproportionation.

Disproportionation is a reaction in which a substance is both oxidised and reduced ✔.

Copper(I) oxide has been reduced to copper (Cu: +1 to 0) and oxidised to copper(II) ions (Cu: +1 to +2) ✔.

(b) Using a colorimeter it was found that the 10.0 cm³ of 0.10 M copper(II) ions formed a complex $[Cu(en)_x]^{2+}$ with 20 cm³ of 0.10 M ethane-1,2-diamine (en). Ethane-1,2-diamine is a *bidentate ligand*. **[5]**

A colorimeter (NOT calorimeter) can be used to find the formula of complex ions.

(i) What is meant by a *bidentate ligand*?

Bidentate means a ligand that can form two co-ordinate bonds to a central metal ion ✔.
A ligand is an atom or ion that bonds with a metal ion forming a co-ordinate bond ✔.

(ii) Work out the value of x in $[Cu(en)_x]^{2+}$.

moles of $Cu^{2+} = \dfrac{10 \times 0.1}{1000}$

moles of ethane-1,2-diamine (en) $= \dfrac{20 \times 0.1}{1000}$

ratio Cu^{2+}: en $= 1:2$; formula is $[Cu(en)_2^{2+}]$ ✔

(iii) The complex ion is planar. With the aid of a diagram, suggest the structure of the ion.

✗ ✗

The diagram should have shown two molecules of en attached to the central copper ion.

Exam practice questions

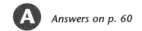

Answers on p. 60

(1) Elements with atomic number 22 to 29 (titanium to copper) are transition metals.

(a) What is a transition metal? **[2]**

(b) Give **three** typical properties of transition metals. **[3]**

(c) What is the electronic structure, in terms of s, p and d orbitals of
(i) chromium **(ii)** copper? **[2]**

(d) Use your answer to **(c)** to explain why **[3]**

    (i) chromium can have an oxidation state of + 6.

    (ii) anhydrous copper(I) chloride is a white solid.

(e) The graph below shows the standard electrode potentials for the cells
$M^{2+}(aq)|M(s)$

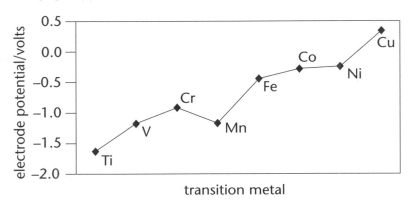

    (i) Write the half-reaction for iron in an $Fe^{2+}(aq)|Fe(s)$ cell. **[1]**

    (ii) Which of the elements Ti to Cu has the greatest reducing power?
       Explain your answer. **[2]**

    (iii) What reaction would take place, if any, if chromium metal were
       added to an aqueous solution of manganese(II) sulphate? Explain
       your answer. **[2]**

(2) Cobalt has an atomic number of 27. Its principal oxidation states are +2 and +3.

(a) Write down the electronic structure of **(i)** Co, **(ii)** Co^{2+}. **[2]**

(b) Give the formula of an ion of another transition element that has the same number of electrons as Co^{2+}. **[1]**

(c) Why is cobalt classified as a transition metal? **[1]**

(d) What is a complex ion? **[2]**

(e) What is the oxidation number and the co-ordination number of cobalt in each of the following complex ions? **[3]**

(i) $[CoCl_4]^{2-}$ **(ii)** $[Co(H_2O)_6]^{2+}$ **(iii)** $[Co(NH_3)_6]^{3+}$

(f) Blue cobalt(II) chloride paper is used as a test for water. The addition of water turns the blue paper pink. The paper goes blue again when the paper is gently heated.

$$[Co(H_2O)_6]^{2+}(aq) + 4Cl^-(aq) \rightleftharpoons [CoCl_4]^{2-}(aq) + 6H_2O(l)$$

Explain, using Le Chatelier's principle, why

(i) the paper goes pink on the addition of water;
(ii) this shows that the forward reaction is endothermic. **[3]**

(g) **(i)** Complete the table below showing the colour of ions **[4]**

ion	colour	ion	colour
$[Mn(H_2O)_6]^{2+}$	pale pink	$[Cr(H_2O)_6]^{3+}$	
MnO_4^-(aq)		$Cr_2O_7^{2-}$(aq)	orange

(ii) Explain, in terms of d orbitals, why transition metal ions are coloured.

Answers

(1) **(a)** an element that has at least one ion with a partially filled d sub-shell.

(b) two or more oxidation states, coloured ions, catalysts.

(c) $Cr = [Ar] 3d^5 4s^1$ $Cu = [Ar] 3d^{10} 4s^1$

(d) (i) Cr can use all 6 electrons from 4s and 3d sub-shells for bonding.

(ii) All the d orbitals in Cu^+ are full.

(e) (i) $Fe^{2+}(aq) + 2e^- \rightleftharpoons Fe(s)$

(ii) Ti. Ti is the most negative $E^\ominus$

(iii) Manganese is more reactive than chromium, therefore no reaction would take place.

(2) **(a) (i)** $[Ar] 3d^7 4s^2$ **(ii)** $[Ar] 3d^7$

(b) Ni^{3+}

(c) it has ions with partially full d orbitals.

(d) a central metal ion surrounded by ligands (ligands are bonded by coordinate bonds).

(e)(i) +2, 4; **(ii)** +2, 6 **(iii)** +3, 6

(f) (i) constraint is water, equilibrium shifts to the left to remove water to form $[Co(H_2O)_6]^{2+}$ which is pink.

(ii) Heating removes the water, therefore equilibrium shifts to the right. Heating moves the equilibrium in the endothermic direction.

(g)(i)

ion	colour	ion	colour
$[Mn(H_2O)_6]^{2+}$	pink	$[Cr(H_2O)_6]^{3+}$	ruby
MnO_4^-	purple	$Cr_2O_7^{2-}(aq)$	orange

(ii) The frequency of the energy absorbed by transfer of electrons between the orbitals of partially filled d sub-shell is in the visible part of the spectrum.

Questions with model answers

C grade candidate – mark scored 6/10

See Revise A2 Study Guide 6.1

(a) In each of parts **(i)** to **(iv)** deduce what you can about benzene and its structure.

Examiner's Commentary

(i) It is a hydrocarbon containing 92.3% by mass of carbon. It has a relative molecular mass of 78. **[2]**

Ratio of C atoms: H atoms = $\frac{92.3}{12} : \frac{7.7}{1} = 7.7 : 7.7 = 1 : 1$
Empirical formula is CH ✔.
Molecular formula = $(CH)_x$ $(12+1)_x = 78$ $x = 6$
Molecular formula C_6H_6 ✔.

(ii) In the presence of ultraviolet light, one mole of benzene reacts with three moles of chlorine Cl_2 to form a single product. **[1]**

Since benzene adds on 3 moles of chlorine it should contain 3 double bonds ✔.

Note the difference in conditions – alkenes react with chlorine at room temperature.

(iii) The length of the C–C single bond is 0.154 nm.; the length of the C–C double bond is 0.134 nm; the six C–C bonds in benzene are of equal length 0.139 nm. **[1]**

The carbon–carbon benzene bond length is between the other lengths, therefore it is neither a single bond nor a double bond ✔.

The electrons are delocalised.

(iv) When 1 mole cyclohexene, C_6H_{10} is reduced by 1 mole of H_2 to cyclohexane the enthalpy change is -119 kJ mol^{-1}. When 1 mole of benzene is reduced to cyclohexane by 3 moles of H_2, the enthalpy change is -207 kJ mol^{-1}. **[2]**

The expected enthalpy change would be $3 \times 119 = -357$ kJ mol^{-1} ✔.
Actual energy change is 150 kJ per mole less than this and hence benzene is more stable ✔.

The value 150 kJ per mole is sometimes referred to as delocalisation, or stabilisation, energy.

(b) An unsaturated aliphatic hydrocarbon **X** has a molecular formula of C_3H_4 Its structure is

$$\underset{H}{\overset{H}{\diagdown}}C=C=C\underset{H}{\overset{H}{\diagup}}$$

Predict, with reasons, **[4]**

It is unsaturated and will change purple aqueous potassium manganate(VII) to colourless.

(i) the reaction between **X** and aqueous potassium manganate(VII) (the products formed are NOT required).

there will be no reaction because the electrons are delocalised ✗

It adds on 2 hydrogen molecules, the predicted enthalpy change is about $2 \times -119 = -238$ kJ mol^{-1}.

(ii) the energy evolved when **X** reacts with excess hydrogen (H_2)

119 kJ of energy taken in ✗.

(iii) whether **X** will show stereoisomerism.

Yes, it contains C=C and therefore will show cis–trans isomerism ✗ ✗.

It will not show cis–trans isomerism because it has two hydrogens on one carbon atom at the end of C=C.

Questions with model answers

A grade candidate – mark scored 8/10

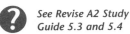 *See Revise A2 Study Guide 5.3 and 5.4*

Methyl methanoate is hydrolysed under acid conditions to form two different organic compounds, each containing one carbon atom. One of the compounds is methanoic acid.

Examiner's Commentary

(a) Name the other compound formed and write the equation for the acid hydrolysis of methyl methanoate. **[2]**

methanol ✔ $HCOOCH_3 + H_2O \rightleftharpoons CH_3OH + HCOOH$ ✔

This is an example of a reversible reaction.

(b) Write an equation to show that methanoic acid is a weak acid. **[1]**

$HCOOH(aq) \rightleftharpoons H^+(aq) + HCOO^-(aq)$ ✔

Weak acids only dissociate slightly when added to water.

(c) Name the product formed when methanoic acid reacts with **(i)** sodium hydroxide **(ii)** ethanol. **[2]**

(i) sodium methanoate ✔ *(ii) ethyl methanoate* ✔.

(d) **(i)** Write the structural formula of an isomer of methyl methanoate. **[1]**

CH_3COOH ✔

Acids and esters are isomers on one another.

(ii) How would you distinguish between the two isomers? **[1]**

Add moist universal indicator paper, methyl methanoate no effect, ethanoic acid will turn it orange/red ✔.

Always look for the simplest test.

(e) Surprisingly, methanoic acid reacts with Tollen's reagent (ammoniacal silver nitrate) to give a silver mirror. **[3]**

(i) Draw the displayed formula of methanoic acid.

$$H-C\overset{\displaystyle O}{\underset{\displaystyle O-H}{<}}$$ ✔

(ii) What would be the shape of a molecule of methanoic acid?

pyramidal ✗.

It is trigonal planar. It has 3 shared 'pairs' of electrons.

(iii) Suggest why methanoic acid gives the silver mirror test.

it contains the carbonyl group ✗.

Methanoic acid contains a CHO group and therefore gives the silver mirror test.

Exam practice questions

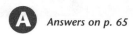 *Answers on p. 65*

(1) The table below gives some values for pK_b at 101 kPa and 298 K. The lower the value of pK_b, the stronger the base.

Name	Formula	pK_b
Ammonia	NH_3	4.8
Methylamine	CH_3NH_2	3.4
Dimethylamine	$(CH_3)_2NH$	3.2
Ethylamine	$C_2H_5NH_2$	3.3
Diethylamine	$(C_2H_5)_2NH$	3.1
Phenylamine	$C_6H_5NH_2$	9.4
Diphenylamine	$(C_6H_5)_2NH$	13.2

(a) Write an equation to show how the strongest base reacts with HCl(aq). **[2]**

(b) Methylamine is formed when bromomethane reacts with excess ammonia. **[2]**

    (i) Why is the other product of the reaction ammonium bromide?

    (ii) Suggest why phenylamine cannot be made by reacting bromobenzene with ammonia.

(c) What does the data tell you about the inductive effects of: **[2]**

    (i) the CH_3 group and the C_2H_5 group

    (ii) the C_6H_5 group?

(d) Why does phenylamine dissolve in hydrochloric acid but not in water? **[3]**

(e) (i) Name a reducing agent that could be used to convert nitrobenzene into phenylamine. **[2]**

    (ii) Outline the preparation of an azo-dye starting from phenylamine. **[4]**

    (iii) Why is it important to keep the temperature below 10°C? **[1]**

Exam practice questions

(2) When benzene is reacted with a mixture of concentrated nitric acid and concentrated sulphuric acid, electrophilic substitution takes place and nitrobenzene is formed as the only product.

(a)   (i) Show how the ion NO_2^+ is formed when sulphuric acid and nitric acid react together.   **[1]**

    (ii) Why is nitric acid behaving as a base in the reaction described in (a)?   **[1]**

    (iii) Why is NO_2^+ described as an electrophile?   **[1]**

    (iv) Using curly arrows, draw a mechanism for the reaction.   **[2]**

(b) (2-Propyl)benzene $C_6H_5CH(CH_3)_2$ can be made by reacting benzene with 2-chloropropane in the presence of a halogen carrier such as iron(III) chloride.

    (i) What is the electrophile in this reaction?   **[1]**

    (ii) Show by means of an equation, how the electrophile named in (b)(i) is formed.   **[1]**

(c) In the presence of ultraviolet light, methylbenzene reacts with chlorine to form dichloromethylbenzene ($C_6H_5CHCl_2$). Dichloromethylbenzene can be hydrolysed to benzaldehyde C_6H_5CHO.

    The formation of dichloromethylbenzene occurs via free radicals.   **[5]**

    (i) Write a mechanism for the reaction.

    (ii) Suggest why one of the products is 1,2-diphenylethane ($C_6H_5CH_2CH_2C_6H_5$).

    (iii) Write the equation for the hydrolysis of dichloromethylbenzene to form benzaldehyde.

Answers

(1) (a) $(C_2H_5)_2NH + HCl \rightarrow (C_2H_5)_2NH_2^+ + Cl^-$

(b)(i) hydrogen bromide reacts with the excess ammonia.

(ii) delocalisation of electrons makes bromobenzene unreactive.

(c)(i) C_2H_5 is slightly greater than CH_3, i.e. it makes the lone pair of electrons on the nitrogen more readily available.

(ii) C_6H_5 withdraws electrons and thus the lone pair of electrons on the nitrogen become less available.

(d) It reacts to form phenylammonium chloride which is ionic. Ionic compounds are soluble in water. Phenylamine is a covalent molecule, which is almost insoluble in polar solvents such as water.

(e)(i) Tin and concentrated hydrochloric acid.

(ii) Make a solution of phenylammonium choride by adding concentrated hydrochloric acid to phenylamine. Add ice-cold sodium nitrite solution (to make benzenediazonium choride). Dissolve phenol in sodium hydroxide solution. Cool in ice. Add the ice-cold benzenediazonium choride.

Examiner's tip

The diazotisation equation is $C_6H_5NH_2 + HNO_2 + HCl \rightarrow C_6H_5N_2^+Cl^- + 2H_2O$.

(iii) Diazonium salts decompose above 10°C.

(2) (a)(i) $HNO_3 + H_2SO_4 \rightarrow H_2NO_3^+ + HSO_4^-$ then $H_2NO_3^+ \rightarrow NO_2^+ + H_2O$

(ii) it is accepting protons from sulphuric acid.

(iii) accepts an electron pair/seeks a source of electrons/it is electron deficient.

(iv)

(b)(i) $(CH_3)_2CH^+$ **(ii)** $FeCl_3 + (CH_3)_2CHCl \rightarrow (CH_3)_2CH^+ + FeCl_4^-$

Examiner's tip

The $FeCl_3$ is a catalyst and is reformed by reacting with H^+ $FeCl_4^- + H^+ \rightarrow FeCl_3 + HCl$.

(c)(i)

$$Cl_2 \rightarrow Cl\bullet + Cl\bullet$$
$$C_6H_5CH_3 + Cl\bullet \rightarrow C_6H_5CH_2\bullet + HCl$$
$$C_6H_5CH_2\bullet + Cl_2 \rightarrow C_6H_5CH_2Cl + Cl\bullet$$
$$C_6H_5CH_2Cl + Cl\bullet \rightarrow C_6H_5CHCl\bullet + HCl$$
$$C_6H_5CHCl\bullet + Cl_2 \rightarrow C_6H_5CHCl_2 + Cl\bullet$$

(ii) $C_6H_5CH_2\bullet + C_6H_5CH_2\bullet \rightarrow C_6H_5CH_2CH_2C_6H_5$.

Examiner's tip

This is one of the termination reactions.

(iii) $C_6H_5CHCl_2 + H_2O \rightarrow C_6H_5CHO + 2HCl$

Questions with model answers

C grade candidate – mark scored 8/14

 See Revise A2 Study Guide 5.1 and 5.2

(a) What is meant by **[4]**

(i) structural isomerism?

> *Two or more compounds having the same molecular formula* ✔
> *but different structural formulae* ✔.

(ii) stereoisomerism?

> *When two or more compounds have the same molecular formula*
> *and the same structural formula* ✔ ✗.

(b) Butan-1-ol is a primary alcohol. Its formula is C_4H_9OH. Draw: **[3]**

(i) another isomer of C_4H_9OH that is a primary alcohol

✗

(ii) optical isomers of C_4H_9OH.

✔ ✔

(c) One of the isomers of C_4H_9OH can be dehydrated to form a hydrocarbon that shows *cis–trans* isomerism.

Draw the displayed formulae of the *cis–trans* isomers of the hydrocarbon. **[3]**

cis   *trans*   ✔ ✔ ✔

(d) Name the isomers below. **[4]**

(i)

> *dimethyl something* ✗   *ethanol* ✗

(ii) Give a chemical test to show how these isomers can be distinguished from one another.

> *Add 2,4 dinitrophenylhydrazine* ✗ ✗.

Examiner's Commentary

There are several types of structural isomers chain, positional and functional group and tautomerism.

There are two types of stereoisomerism: cis-trans and optical.

You should have added 'but different spatial arrangements of their bonds'.

You have drawn a secondary alcohol.

C_4H_9OH also forms a secondary and a tertiary isomer.

Learn how to name organic compounds. These are propanone and propanal.

This is a test for the carbonyl group. You should have added Benedict's solution and heated: propanal gives a brick-red precipitate, propanone has no effect.

A grade candidate – mark scored 12/15

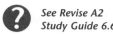

See Revise A2 Study Guide 6.6

Examiner's Commentary

(a) Using chloroethene, ethane-1,2-diol and benzene-1,4-dicarboxylic acid explain what is meant by:

(i) addition polymerisation **[2]**

The formation of a polymer by an addition reaction ✔.
Chloroethene polymerises to form poly(chloroethene) ✔.

The monomer is unsaturated, the polymer is saturated.

(ii) condensation polymerisation. **[2]**

The formation of a polymer by elimination of small molecules such as water or ammonia from monomers ✔.
ethane-1,2-diol and benzene-1,4-dicarboxylic acid eliminate water ✔.

The small molecule eliminated is water.

(b) Explain why monomers are gases or volatile liquids, whereas polymers are solids. **[2]**

Monomers are small molecules with low relative molecular masses and very small van der Waals forces between the molecules ✔. *Polymers have very large molecular masses and large van der Waals forces* ✔.

(c) Hexane-1,6-dioyl chloride reacts with 1,6-diaminohexane to form a polyamide with the formula $\text{-[OC-(CH}_2)_x\text{-CO-NH-(CH}_2)_y\text{-NH]-}_n$

(i) What name is given to the CONH link that is found in proteins? **[1]**

Peptide link ✔.

This is important – found in living things.

(ii) What are the values of '*x*' and '*y*' in this formula? **[2]**

$x = 6$ ✗ *and* $y = 6$ ✔.

In the value for 'x', you have included the carbon from the COCl. x = 4

(d) **(i)** A hydrocarbon polymer **X** was found to contain 85.7% by mass of carbon. What is the empirical formula of **X**? **[2]**

$\frac{85.7}{12} : \frac{14.3}{1}$ ✔ $= 7.14 : 14.3$ *i.e.* $1 : 2$

Empirical formula is CH_2 ✔.

(ii) Complete combustion of 7.143×10^{-5} moles of **X** produces 0.07143 moles of carbon dioxide. It was found that 0.107 moles of oxygen (O_2) were used up for the complete combustion. What is the formula of **X**? **[3]**

1 mole of X gives $\frac{0.07143}{0.00007143} = 1000$ *moles of carbon dioxide* ✔ ✔ ✗.

1 mole of X reacts with 1500 moles of oxygen to form 1000 moles of carbon dioxide. Hence 1000 moles of water are formed. The number of hydrogen atoms is 2000. Formula is $C_{1000}H_{2000}$.

(iii) Give the displayed formula of the simplest monomer of the hydrocarbon from which **X** can be made. **[1]**

✗

Monomer would be ethene

$$\begin{array}{c} H \\ \diagdown \\ H \diagup \end{array} C = C \begin{array}{c} H \\ \diagup \\ \diagdown H \end{array}$$

Exam practice questions

A *Answers on p. 70*

(1) Illustrated below are two different synthesis routes

$$CH_3CH_2CH_2OH \xrightarrow[\text{reflux}]{A + K_2Cr_2O_7} CH_3CH_2COOH \xrightarrow[\text{u v light}]{B} \boxed{X} \xrightarrow[\text{heat}]{C} CH_3CH(OH)COOH$$

$$\boxed{Y} \xrightarrow[\text{heat}]{HNO_3 + D} C_6H_5NO_2 \xrightarrow[\text{heat}]{E + F} C_6H_5NH_2 \xrightarrow[\text{ice cold}]{HNO_2 + HCl} \boxed{Z}$$

(a) What are the missing reagents **A, B, C, D, E** and **F**? **[6]**

(b) Draw the structure of compounds **X, Y** and **Z**. **[3]**

(c) State, with a reason, which of the compounds $CH_3CH_2CH_2OH$, CH_3CH_2COOH, $CH_3CH(OH)COOH$, $C_6H_5NO_2$ or $C_6H_5NH_2$ shows optical isomerism. **[2]**

(2) **X** is a primary amide containing 49.3% carbon, 9.6% hydrogen, 19.2% nitrogen and 21.9% oxygen.

(a) What is the empirical formula of **X**? **[3]**

The mass spectrum for **X** is shown below.

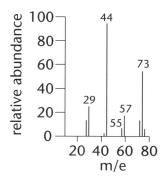

(b) **(i)** What is the M_r of **X**? **[1]**

(ii) What is the molecular formula of **X**? **[1]**

(iii) Show the most likely structure of **X**. **[2]**

(c) Write down the formulae of the fragment ions with an m/e value of **(i)** 29 **(ii)** 44. **[2]**

(d) There is a very small peak at m/e 74 due to the presence of ^{13}C in the molecule. Suggest why the height of this peak indicates the number of carbon atoms in the molecule. **[1]**

(e) The infrared spectrum of **X** is:

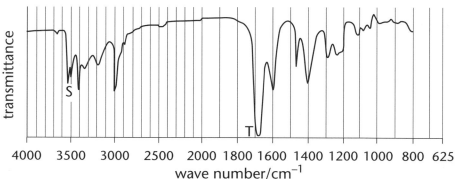

(i) From the above spectrum how can you tell that **X** is **NOT** a carboxylic acid? **[1]**

(ii) Identify the groups responsible for the absorption at **S** and **T**. **[2]**

(f) How many peaks will compound **X** show in a low resolution nuclear magnetic resonance spectrum? **[1]**

Answers

(1) (a)   **A** = sulphuric acid   **B** = chlorine   **C** = sodium hydroxide (aq)

D = concentrated sulphuric acid   **E** = tin   **F** = hydrochloric acid

(b)

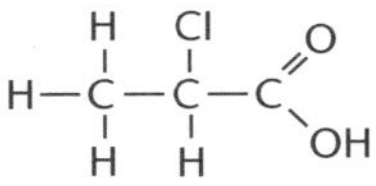

X 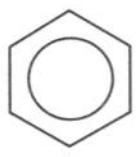   Y 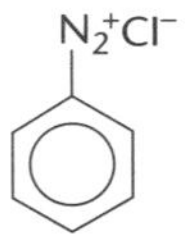   Z

(c) $CH_3CH(OH)COOH$ = 2 hydroxypropanoic acid. It has a chiral carbon atom.

Examiner's tip

The chiral carbon has four different groups attached to it: CH_3, COOH, OH and H.

(2) (a)   C $\frac{49.3}{12}$ H $\frac{9.6}{1}$ N $\frac{19.2}{14}$ O $\frac{21.9}{16}$

4.11 : 9.6 : 1.37 : 1.37 = 3 : 7 : 1 : 1

Empirical formula is C_3H_7NO.

(b)(i) 73

Examiner's tip

Largest m/e with highest peak is the M_r.

(ii) C_3H_7NO

(iii)

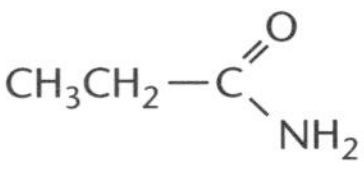

(c)(i) $C_2H_5^+$ **(ii)** $CONH_2^+$

Examiner's tip

The molecules fragment in the mass spectrometer. This gives an indication of the structure.

(d)   Two carbon atoms in the molecule give a peak which will be twice the height of one carbon atom in the molecule.

(e)(i) No broad band between 2500 and 3500 cm^{-1}.
(ii) S is NH_2 and T is C=O

Examiner's tip

The absorptions indicate the groups present. The 3400 to 3500 cm^{-1} indicates N–H.
3000 cm^{-1} is C–H and 1700 cm^{-1} is C=O

(f)   3.

Examiner's tip

There are three environments carrying hydrogen, therefore 3 peaks.

Questions with model answers

C grade candidate – mark scored 6/12

*See Revise A2
Study Guide 8*

Hydrogen peroxide (H_2O_2) is a pale blue viscous liquid.

Examiner's Commentary

(a) Using a dot and cross diagram show the electronic structure of hydrogen peroxide. **[2]**

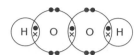

✔ ✔

The shape is based on tetrahedrals.

(b) Hydrogen peroxide can act as a reducing agent. In the presence of an acid, it reduces the manganate(VII) ion (MnO_4^-) to the manganese(II) ion (Mn^{2+}). Hydrogen peroxide is oxidised to oxygen. **[4]**

(i) Suggest why the solution is NOT acidified with hydrochloric acid.

It is a strong acid ✗ ✗.

Hydrochloric acid would be oxidised to chlorine by MnO_4^-.

(ii) Write the equation for the reaction between hydrogen peroxide and acidified manganate(VII) ions.

$5H_2O_2(aq) + 2MnO_4^-(aq) + 6H^+(aq) \rightarrow$
$2Mn^{2+}(aq) + 5O_2(g) + 3H_2O(l)$ ✔ ✗

You appear to have forgotten the hydrogen from hydrogen peroxide.

(c) The rate of the catalytic decomposition of H_2O_2 solution into water and oxygen can be found by taking equal volumes of H_2O_2 after known intervals of time. These portions are titrated with standard potassium manganate(VII) solution.

The results from such an experiment are shown below. **[6]**

Time/min	0	5	10	15	20	25
Volume of standard $KMnO_4$ used/cm³	25.0	19.8	15.8	12.5	9.9	7.9

(i) Why is the volume of $KMnO_4$ used a measure of the concentration of the H_2O_2?

2 moles of $KMnO_4$ is equivalent to 5 moles of H_2O_2 ✔.

(ii) Show that the reaction is first order with respect to H_2O_2.

initial concentration of H_2O_2 is proportional to 25.0 cm³ of $KMnO_4$ ✔.

It takes 15 minutes for concentration to fall to 12.5 cm³ ✔ ✗.

You should have confirmed with another pair of results.

(iii) For a first order reaction half-life $(t_{\frac{1}{2}}) = \dfrac{0.693}{k}$

Calculate the rate constant k for this reaction.

✗ ✗.

Answer was 0.046 min⁻¹.

Questions with model answers

? For help see Revise A2 Study Guide 8

A grade candidate – mark scored 8/10

Examiner's Commentary

Phenylethene (styrene) has the structure:

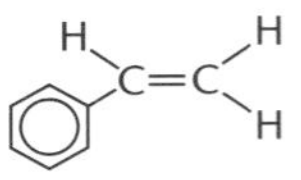

(a) What is the empirical formula of phenylethene? **[1]**

CH ✔.

The molecular formula is C_8H_8.

(b) One method of preparation of phenylethene is from an alcohol with the molecular formula $C_8H_{10}O$.

(i) Draw **two** structural isomers that are aromatic alcohols with the molecular formula $C_8H_{10}O$. **[2]**

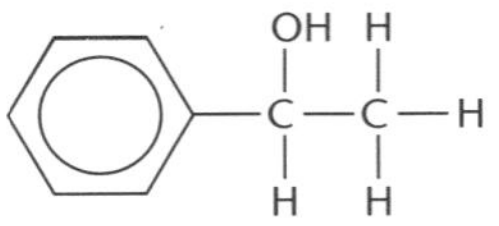

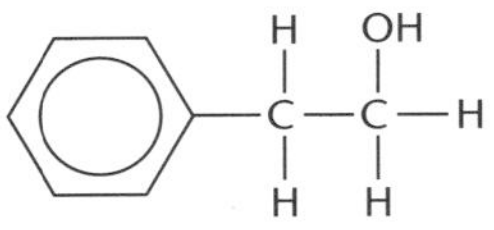

(ii) Explain why only one of the isomers in **(i)** above has optical isomers. **[1]**

Only the structure on the left has a carbon atom with four different groups attached to it ✔.

(c) Phenylethene is an important chemical. Industrially it is made from benzene in two stages:

I   Benzene reacts with ethene in the presence of an acid. The acid is needed to react with ethene to produce a carbonium ion, which then reacts with benzene in the presence of boron trifluoride, BF_3. The product is ethylbenzene.

II   Ethylbenzene is dehydrogenated at 600°C in the presence of iron(III) oxide as catalyst to form phenylethene.

(i) Write equations to show stages I and II. **[2]**

$C_6H_6 + C_2H_4 \rightarrow C_6H_5C_2H_5$ ✔

$C_6H_5C_2H_5 \rightarrow C_6H_5CH{=}CH_2 + H_2$ ✔

Combining these equations it can be seen that one mole of benzene produces one mole of phenylethene.

(ii) How would you distinguish, by a chemical test, between benzene and phenylethene? **[3]**

Add bromine water ✔ the bromine will change from orange/brown to colourless with phenylethene ✔. ✗

You should have said that there was no reaction between benzene and bromine.

(d) Why does poly(phenylethene) NOT have an exact relative molecular mass? **[1]**

It contains a large number of isotopes ✗.

The polymer chains are of variable length.

Exam practice questions

 Answers on p. 74

(1) (a) Using water, describe (with examples if necessary) what is meant by: **[10]**

    (i) hydrogen bonding — *the type of bond between electronegative elements and s* elements *like permanent dipole interaction between O and H_2 in H_2O*

    (ii) oxidation — *Increase oxidation number*

    (iii) acid — *molecule with H^+ ion / proton donors*

    (iv) polar — *molecule where atoms have a slight charge, in water $O = \delta^-$ $H = \delta^+$*

    (v) ligand.

(b) The ionic product of water at various temperatures is given in the table below.

Temperature/°C	0	10	20	30	40	50
$K_w/10^{-14}$ mol^2 dm^{-6}	0.15	0.29	0.68	1.47	2.92	5.45

    (i) Define K_w. **[1]**

    (ii) Draw a graph of K_w against temperature. **[3]**

    (iii) Use your graph to predict
        • the temperature at which the pH of water is 7
        • the pH of water at 45°C. **[4]**

(c) The dynamic equilibrium for the hydrolysis of bismuth(III) chloride is summarised below. Bismuth oxychloride, BiOCl, is a white solid.

$$BiCl_3(aq) + H_2O(l) \rightleftharpoons BiOCl(s) + 2H^+(aq) + 2Cl^-(aq)$$

    (i) What is meant by '*dynamic equilibrium*'? **[2]**

Predict, with reasons, what you would see if:

    (ii) water were added to a solution of bismuth(III) chloride. *Formation of a solid precipitate as $BiOCl$ is (s)* **[2]**

    (iii) concentrated hydrochloric acid were added to bismuth oxychloride. **[2]**

(d) The table below gives values for some average bond energies.

bond energy /kJ mol^{-1}	436	496	463
bond	H–H	O=O	O–H

Calculate the enthalpy change of formation of steam. **[4]**

Answers

(1) (a)(i) A strong dipole–dipole interaction between water molecules in which hydrogen is bonded to the highly electronegative O atom in another water molecule.

(ii) Oxidation is an increase in oxidation number. When sodium is added to water, the sodium is oxidised by water to sodium ion, Na^+ (i.e. its oxidation number increases from 0 to +1).

(iii) Acids are proton donors. When ammonia is added to water, water donates a proton to ammonia to form the ammonium ion.

(iv) The electrons are shared unevenly in a covalent bond. Oxygen is more electronegative than hydrogen and thus has a greater share of the electrons.

(v) Using one of the lone pairs of electrons in oxygen, a water molecule forms a dative covalent bond with a central metal ion.

(b)(i) $K_w = [H^+][OH^-]$

(ii)

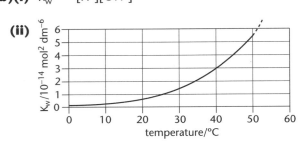

(iii) pH = 7 at 24–26°C
At 45°C: $K_w = 4 \times 10^{-14}$ mol²dm⁻⁶ therefore $[H^+] = 2 \times 10^{-7}$; pH = 6.7

(c)(i) The rate of the forward reaction equals the rate of the reverse reaction.

(ii) A white precipitate of BiOCl solid would form, excess water moves the equilibrium to the right.

(iii) The solution goes clear, H^+ ions shift the equilibrium to the left.

(d) $H_2(g) + \frac{1}{2}O_2 \rightarrow H_2O(g)$

Energy required to break bonds = 436 + 248 = 684 kJ
Energy given out when bonds are made = 2 × –463 = –926 kJ
Enthalpy change is = –926 + 684 = –242 kJ mol⁻¹

Mock Exam

Answer all the questions   Time: 2 hours

(1) Lithium exists naturally as a mixture of isotopes.

(a) Explain the term *isotopes*.

An element with the same number of protons and electrons but different number of neutrons **[1]**

(b) Which isotope is used as the standard against which relative atomic masses are measured?

^{12}C **[1]**

(c) A sample of lithium has the following percentage composition by mass: ^{6}Li, 7.4%; ^{7}Li, 92.6%

(i) Use this information to help you complete the table below.

isotope	number of	
	protons	neutrons
^{6}Li	3	3
^{7}Li	3	4

[2]

(ii) Calculate the relative atomic mass of this lithium sample. Your answer should be given to three significant figures. **[2]**

$$0.074 \times 6 = 0.444$$
$$0.926 \times 7 = 6.482$$

$$6.482 + 0.444 = 6.926$$
$$= 6.93 \text{ to } 3sf$$

[2]

(d) Relative atomic masses can be determined using a mass spectrometer. State the main processes that take place in the four regions shown below.

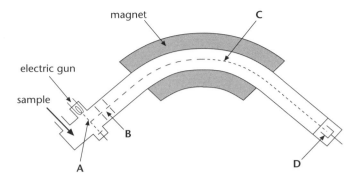

A.. **[1]**

B.. **[1]**

C.. **[1]**

D.. **[1]**

[Total: 10]

(2) Magnesium oxide, MgO, is an ionic compound. This question looks at two reactions in which magnesium oxide is a product.

(a) Magnesium oxide can be formed by heating magnesium in oxygen.

(i) Complete the electronic configuration for a magnesium atom.

$1s^2$ $2s^2 2p^6 3s^2$ .... **[1]**

(ii) Complete the electronic configuration for a magnesium ion.

$1s^2$ $2s^2 2p^6$ .... **[1]**

(iii) Write an equation, including state symbols, for the reaction of magnesium with oxygen.

.... $2Mg_{(s)} + O_{2(g)} \rightarrow 2MgO_{(s)}$ .... **[2]**

(iv) Draw a 'dot-and-cross' diagram of magnesium oxide.

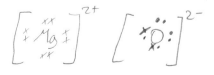

[2]

(b)   Magnesium oxide can be made by heating magnesium nitrate.
A student decomposed 4.50 g of $Mg(NO_3)_2$ as in the equation below.
(A_r; Mg, 24·3; N, 14·0; O, 16·0)
$2Mg(NO_3)_2(s) \rightarrow 2MgO(s) + 4NO_2(g) + O_2(g)$

(i) Calculate how many moles of $Mg(NO_3)_2$ were heated.

$24.3 + (14 \times 2) + (16 \times 6) = 148.3g\ mol^{-1}$

$\dfrac{4.5}{148.3} = 0.0303343897\ moles$

$= 0.03\ moles$

[2]

(ii) Calculate the mass of MgO that was formed.

$0.0303 \times (24.3 + 16) = 1.22109$

$= 1.22g$

[2]

(iii) Calculate the total volume of gases formed. Assume that the gas
volumes were measured at room temperature and pressure, (r.t.p.).
1 mol of gas molecules has a volume of 24.0 dm³ at r.t.p.

$volume = \dfrac{moles}{24000}$ $volume\ of\ O_2 = \dfrac{(0.0303 \div 2)}{24000} = 6.3125 \times 10^{-7} cm^3$ or

$6.3125 \times 10^{-4}\ dm^3$

$volume\ of\ NO_2 = \dfrac{(0.0303 \times 2)}{24000} = 2.525 \times 10^{-6} cm^3$ or

$2.525 \times 10^{-3}\ dm^3$

[2]

(iv) This is a redox reaction. Identify the element that has been reduced and
state its oxidation states before and after the reaction.

element reduced ....Oxygen..

oxidation state before reaction ....O...

oxidation state after reaction...............−2.. **[3]**

[Total: 15]

(3) The chemistry of ammonia, NH_3, is influenced by its polarity and its ability to form hydrogen bonds.

(a) Polarity can be explained in terms of electronegativity.

(i) Explain the term *electronegativity*.

....

....

.... [2]

(ii) Why are ammonia molecules polar?

....

.... [1]

(b) The polarity of NH_3 molecules results in the formation of hydrogen bonds.

(i) Draw a diagram to show hydrogen bonding between two molecules of NH_3. Your diagram should include dipoles and lone pairs of electrons.

[3]

(ii) State the H—N—H bond angle in an ammonia molecule.

.... [1]

(c) Ammonia reacts with hydrochloric acid, forming the ammonium ion NH_4^+.

(i) State the H—N—H bond angle in an ammonium ion.

.... [1]

(ii) Explain why the H—N—H bond angle changes during this reaction.

....

....

.... [3]

[Total: 11]

(4) The atomic radii of the elements Li to F and Na to Cl are shown in the table below.

element	Li	Be	B	C	N	O	F
atomic radius/nm	0.134	0.125	0.090	0.077	0.075	0.073	0.071
element	Na	Mg	Al	Si	P	S	Cl
atomic radius/nm	0.154	0.145	0.130	0.118	0.110	0.102	0.099

(a) Explain what causes the general **decrease** in atomic radii across each period?

Greater number of protons across the period so electrons are attracted more strongly so atomic radii decrease [3]

(b) Explain what causes the general **increase** in atomic radii down each group.

Extra electron orbital as you go down the group, so more shielding, less attraction by ~~nucleus~~ protons in nucleus [3]

(c) The first ionisation energy of aluminium is +578 kJ mol^{-1}.

(i) Write an equation, with state symbols, for the change that corresponds to the first ionisation energy of aluminium.

$Al_{(g)} \rightarrow Al^+_{(g)} + e^-$ [2]

(ii) The first ionisation energy of magnesium is +738 kJ mol^{-1}.
Explain why, despite having smaller atoms, the first ionisation energy of aluminium is less than that of magnesium.

Mg has 3s orbital as outer orbital, Al has 3p orbital so more shielding in Al so easier to remove electron [2]

[Total: 10]

(5) Chlorine and its compounds have many uses. Chlorine bleach is used to kill bacteria.

(a) Chlorine bleach is made by the reaction of chlorine with aqueous sodium hydroxide.

$$Cl_2(g) + 2NaOH(aq) \rightarrow NaClO(aq) + NaCl(aq) + H_2O(l)$$

Determine the oxidation number of chlorine in

Cl_2.............. 0 ....

NaClO.......... +1 ....

NaCl.......... −1 .... [3]

(b) In solution, chlorine oxidises bromide ions to bromine.
Construct a balanced ionic equation for this reaction.

.... $Cl_{2(g)} + 2Br^-_{(aq)} \rightarrow 2Cl^-_{(aq)} + Br_{2(g)}$ .... [1]

(c) Describe a simple test for the presence of a chloride ion. You should write an ionic equation as part of your answer.

test............ Test with silver nitrate A white ....

.... precipitate should form ....

equation.......... $Ag^+_{(aq)} + Cl^-_{(aq)} \rightarrow AgCl(s)$ .... [3]

(d) Relate the **physical** properties of Cl_2 and NaCl to their structure and bonding.

.... Cl_2 has molecular structure and is linked by covalent ....
.... bonds. Hence it has a lower melting and boiling ....
.... point than NaCl which is an ionic compound ....
.... that has a strong lattice structure. As NaCl ....
.... is ionic it can conduct electricity when molten ....
.... Cl_2 cannot as it does not have positive and ....
.... negative ions. NaCl is solid at room temperature ....
.... and pressure, Cl_2 is a gas due to weak intermolecular ....
.... forces and low melting / boiling point of Cl_2. [8]

NaCl is soluble in water as it is ionic
and will form an alkaline solution.
Chlorine will react with water to
form an acidic solution.

[Total: 15]

(6) Hydrocarbons, such as heptane C_7H_{16}, are used as fuels making use of their combustion reaction with oxygen. Polluting gases such as NO and NO_2 are also made during combustion in the petrol engines of cars.

(a) Write a balanced equation for the complete combustion of heptane.

.... [1]

(b) (i) Explain the term *enthalpy change of formation*.

....

....

.... [2]

(ii) What conditions are needed for this to be a *standard* enthalpy change?

....

.... [2]

(iii) Write an equation to represent the enthalpy change of formation of $NO_2(g)$.

.... [2]

(c) Modern cars have 'catalytic converters' in their exhausts to convert nitrogen oxides into less harmful substances. One reaction that occurs is as follows:
$$4CO + 2NO_2 \rightarrow 4CO_2 + N_2$$
Use the data below to calculate the enthalpy change of this reaction.

compound	ΔH_f/kJ mol^{-1}
NO_2	+33
CO	−111
CO_2	−394

[3]

(d) The oxides of nitrogen only form at high temperatures such as during lightning strikes or in internal combustion engines. Describe how the Boltzmann distribution can help to explain why a temperature rise leads to an increased rate of reaction. Use the axes below to support your answer.

....

....

.... **[3]**

[Total: 13]

(7) This question refers to the hydrogen halides HF and HCl. The table below lists some bond enthalpies which are required in different parts of this question.

bond	average bond energy/kJ mol^{-1}
F–F	+158
Cl–Cl	+244
H–F	+568
H–Cl	+432

(a) Explain the term *bond enthalpy*.

....

....

.... **[2]**

(b) The hydrogen halides HCl and HF can be made from their elements. The formation of HCl is exothermic:

$$H_2(g) + Cl_2(g) \rightarrow 2HCl(g) \qquad \Delta H = -184 \text{ kJ mol}^{-1}$$

(i) Show that the bond enthalpy of the H–H bond is +436 kJ mol^{-1}.

[2]

(ii) Calculate the enthalpy change for the formation of HF from its elements.

$$H_2(g) + F_2(g) \rightarrow 2HF(g)$$

[2]

(c)   The reaction between hydrogen and chlorine to form hydrogen chloride is exothermic.

   (i)   Explain why no reaction takes place unless the reactants are sparked.

   ....

   ....

   .... [2]

   (ii)   Draw an enthalpy profile diagram to support your answer in (c)(i).

   [3]

   [Total: 11]

(8)   Ammonia, NH_3, is manufactured by the Haber process in an exothermic equilibrium reaction.

$$N_2(g) + 3H_2(g) \rightleftharpoons 2NH_3(g) \quad \Delta H = -92 \text{ kJ mol}^{-1}$$

(a)   Describe and explain the effect of pressure on the **rate** of this reaction.

   ....

   ....

   .... [2]

(b)   Describe and explain how the **equilibrium position** of this reaction is affected by

   (i)   increasing the temperature,

   ....

   ....

   .... [2]

   (ii)   increasing the pressure.

   ....

   ....

   .... [2]

(c) Why is the temperature used described as a compromise?

Compromise between yield of ammonia and rate of reaction. Fast rate of reaction and [2]
sufficient yield of ammonia for it to be economically viable.

[Total: 8]

(9) The hydrocarbons in crude oil can be separated by fractional distillation.

(a) Explain in terms of forces why fractional distillation separates the hydrocarbons in crude oil.

Different fractions boil off at different temperature, shorter chain hydrocarbons have weaker and fewer bonds to be broken, van der Waals forces between molecules also boil off quicker [2] *than larger hydrocarbon fractions*

(b) The alkanes are an example of a homologous series.

(i) Explain the term *homologous series*.

....

....

.... **[2]**

(ii) What is the general formula for the alkanes?

$C_n H_{2n+2}$ **[1]**

(iii) What is the formula of the alkane with 15 carbon atoms?

$C_{15} H_{32}$ **[1]**

(iv) Calculate the relative molecular mass of pentane.

72 **[1]**

(c) Nonane, C_9H_{20}, can be isolated by fractional distillation and then cracked into hexane and compound **A**.

(i) Write a balanced equation to represent this cracking of nonane.

$C_9 H_{20} \longrightarrow C_6 H_{14} + C_3 H_6$ **[1]**

(ii) Name compound **A**.

propene **[1]**

(iii) Explain why the cracking of hydrocarbons is such an important process.

Produces unsaturated compounds like alkenes which can be used to make polymers like PVC for plastics and other products. **[2]**

[Total: 11]

(10) Two reactions of but-1-ene, C_4H_8, are shown below

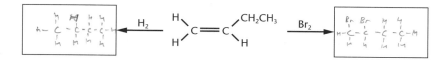

(a) Draw structures for the products of these two reactions in the boxes above. **[2]**

(b) For the reaction between but-1-ene and bromine

    (i) name the type of reaction that takes place,

        Addition reaction **[1]**

    (ii) what type of reagent is bromine?

        Electrophile **[1]**

    (iii) complete the mechanism below.

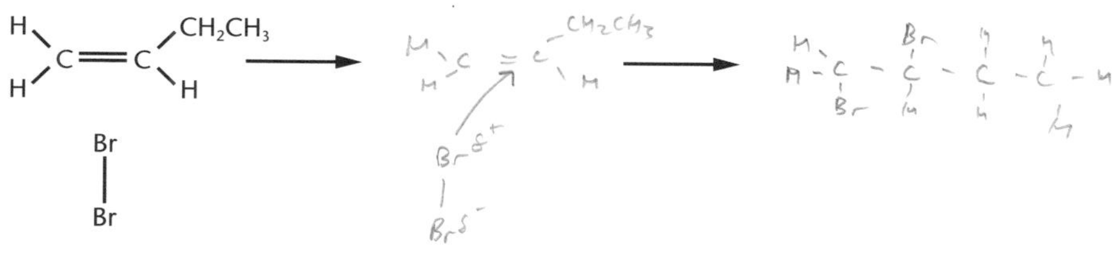

[3]

(c) But-1-ene reacts with steam in the presence of an acid catalyst to form a mixture of two alcohols. Draw the structure of the two alcohols in the boxes below.

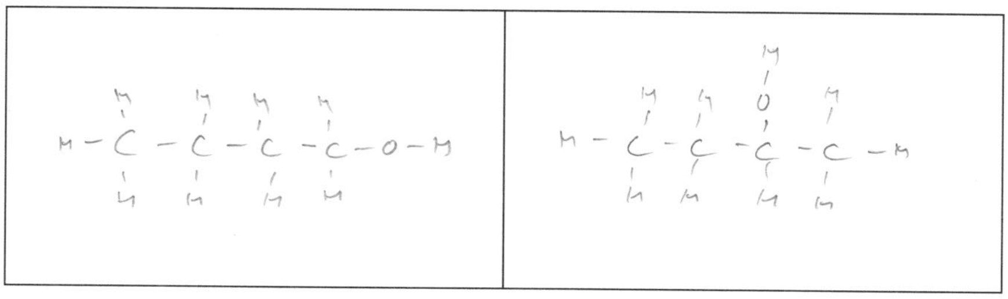

[2]

(d) But-1-ene can be polymerised into poly(but-1-ene).

(i) What type of polymerisation forms poly(but-1-ene)?

.... *Addition polymerisation* .... **[1]**

(ii) Draw a section of poly(but-1-ene) to show **two** repeat units.

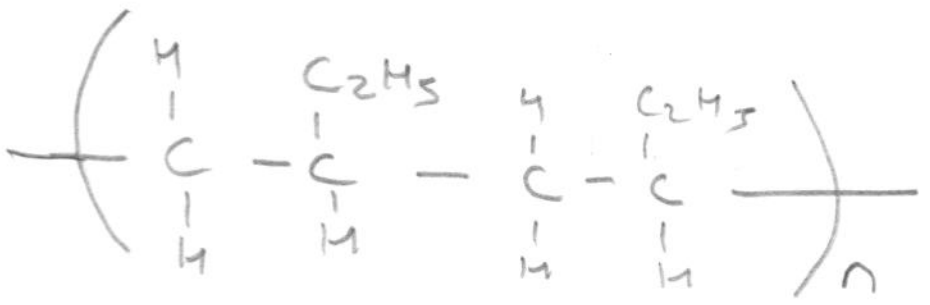

[handwritten polymer structure showing repeat units with C_2H_5 side groups]

[1]

[Total : 11]

(11) Butane, C_4H_{10}, reacts with Cl_2 in the presence of sunlight to form a mixture of chlorinated products, including C_4H_9Cl, formed as shown in the following equation.

$$C_4H_{10} + Cl_2 \rightarrow C_4H_9Cl + HCl$$

(a) Write equations for the following stages in the mechanism of this reaction.

initiation .... $Cl_2 \xrightarrow{\text{UV light}} Cl\cdot + Cl\cdot$ ....

propagation .... $C_4H_{10} + Cl\cdot \rightarrow C_4H_9\cdot + HCl$ ....

.... $(C_4H_9\cdot + 2Cl \rightarrow C_4H_9Cl + Cl\cdot)$ ....

termination .... $C_4H_9\cdot + Cl\cdot \rightarrow C_4H_9Cl$ .... **[4]**

(b) Compound **A** is one of two possible structural isomers of C_4H_9Cl. Compound **A** was reacted in the sequence shown below.

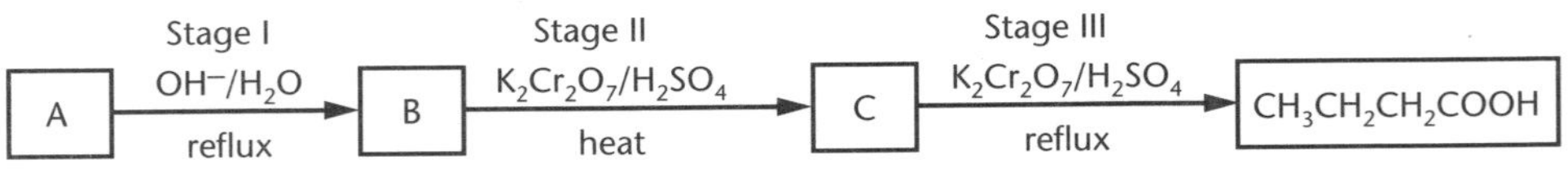

Stage I		Stage II		Stage III	
A	$\xrightarrow[\text{reflux}]{OH^-/H_2O}$	B	$\xrightarrow[\text{heat}]{K_2Cr_2O_7/H_2SO_4}$	C	$\xrightarrow[\text{reflux}]{K_2Cr_2O_7/H_2SO_4}$	$CH_3CH_2CH_2COOH$

(i) Identify compounds **A**, **B** and **C**.

1-chlorobutane	butan-1-ol	butanal
$CH_3CH_2CH_2CH_2Cl$	$CH_3CH_2CH_2CH_2OH$	$CH_3CH_2CH_2CHO$
compound **A**	compound **B**	compound **C**

[3]

(ii) Explain the role of the hydroxide ion, OH^- in stage I above.

.... *Acts as a nucleophile to attack carbocation* ....

.... *adjacent to chlorine atom thereby displacing/substituting* .... **[2]**

.... *Cl^- ion.*

(iii) For stage II above, state what colour changes take place in the reaction mixture.

from........*orange*........... to ....*green*........................... **[2]**

(iv) Write a balanced equation for the oxidation of **B** to **C**. The oxidising agent can be represented as [O] in your equation.

$$CH_3CH_2CH_2CH_2OH + [O] \rightarrow CH_3CH_2CH_2C\overset{HO}{\diagdown} + H_2O + [O]$$ **[1]**

(c) Organic compounds containing halogens have many uses. Compound **A**, a compound in a dry-cleaning solvent, has the percentage composition by mass: Cl, 41.6%; C, 14.0%; F, 44.4%. The relative molecular mass of compound **A** is 171.

(i) Calculate the molecular formula of compound **A**.

$$\frac{41.6}{35.5} = 1.17 \qquad \begin{array}{l} 1:1:2 \\ Cl:C:F \end{array} \qquad CClF_2 = 85.5$$

$$\frac{14}{12} = 1.17 \qquad\qquad 85.5 \times 2 = 171$$

$$\frac{44.4}{19} = 2.33$$

$$C_2Cl_2F_4$$

[3]

(ii) Suggest a possible structure for compound **A**. Name your structure.

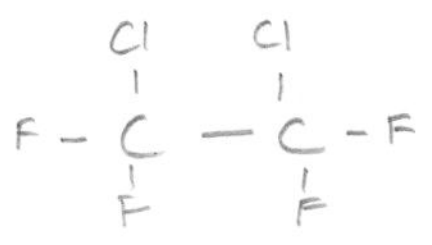

name...........*1,2 dichloro 1,1,2,2 tetrafluoroethane*............. **[2]**

[Total: 17]

Answers

(1) (a) Atoms of the same element with different numbers of neutrons

(b) carbon-12

(c) (i) ^6Li: $3p^+$, $3n$; ^7Li: $3p^+$, $4n$

(ii) $\dfrac{7.4 \times 6}{100} + \dfrac{92.6 \times 7}{100}$ = 6.926 = 6.93 (to 3 sig figs)

(d) **A**: ionisation; **B** acceleration; **C** deflection; **D**: detection

(2) (a) (i) $1s^2\,2s^2\,2p^6\,3s^2$

(ii) $1s^2\,2s^2\,2p^6$

(iii) $2Mg(s) + O_2(g) \rightarrow 2MgO(s)$

(iv) dot and cross; charges

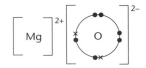

(b) (i) molar mass of $Mg(NO_3)_2$ = 148.3 g mol^{-1}

moles $Mg(NO_3)_2$ = $\dfrac{4.50}{148.3}$ = 3.03×10^{-2} mol

(ii) molar mass of MgO = 40.3 g mol^{-1}
mass MgO = $3.03 \times 10^{-2} \times 40.3$ = 1.22 g

(iii) moles of NO_2 and O_2 molecules = $\dfrac{5}{2} \times 3.03 \times 10^{-2}$

volume gas = $24.0 \times \dfrac{5}{2} \times 3.03 \times 10^{-2}$ = 1.82 dm^3

(iv) element reduced: N;
oxidation state: before reaction: +5; after reaction: +4

(3) (a) (i) attraction (of an atom) for electrons in a (covalent) bond.

(ii) N and H have different electronegativities

(b) (i) dipole; H bond; involvement of lone pair

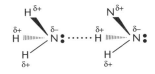

(ii) 107°

(c) (i) 109.5°

(ii) NH_3 has 3 bonded pairs and a lone pair of electrons
NH_4^+ has 4 bonded pairs
lone pair has a greater repelling effect than bonding pair

(4) (a) The nuclear charge increases as electrons are added to same shell. The electrons experience greater attraction, reducing atomic radius

(b) The number of shells increases. Electronic shielding increases. Electrons experience less attraction, increasing atomic radius.

(c) (i) $Al(g) \rightarrow Al^+(g) + e^-$

(ii) In Al, highest energy electron is in 3p orbital. In Mg, highest energy electron is in 3s orbital. 3p has a higher energy than 3s.

(5) (a) (i) Cl_2: 0; NaClO: +1; NaCl: −1

(b) $Cl_2 + 2Br^- \rightarrow Br_2 + 2Cl^-$

(c) *test*: Add $AgNO_3(aq)$. White precipitate forms
equation: $Ag^+(aq) + Cl^-(aq) \rightarrow AgCl(s)$

(d) For Cl_2 and for NaCl, any **two properties** only.
Cl_2: poor conductor of electricity : no mobile electrons or ions :
low m/bt pt : weak intermolecular or van der Waals forces :
soluble in non-polar solvents : which interact with non-polar Cl_2
NaCl: conducts only when aq or molten : when ions are mobile :
high m/bt pt : strong forces between ions/giant ionic lattice :
soluble in polar solvents : dipoles interact with ions

(6) (a) $C_7H_{16}(l) + 11O_2(g) \rightarrow 7CO_2(g) + 8H_2O(l)$

(b) (i) The enthalpy change that accompanies the formation of 1 mole of a compound from its constituent elements

(ii) 100 kPa and a stated temperature, usually 298 K

(iii) $\frac{1}{2}N_2(g) + O_2(g) \rightarrow NO_2(g)$
reactants and products forming 1 mol NO_2

(c) $\Delta H = 4 \times -394 - (4 \times -111 + 2 \times +33)$
$= -1198 \text{ kJ mol}^{-1}$

(d)

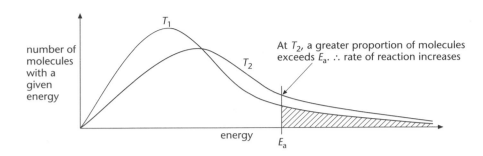

At a higher temperature, a larger proportion of molecules exceeds the activation energy of the reaction

(7) (a) Bond enthalpy is the enthalpy change required to break and separate 1 mole of bonds in the molecules of a gaseous element or compound so that the resulting gaseous species exert no forces upon each other.

(b)(i) bond enthalpy(H–H) $= -184 - 244 + (2 \times 432) = +436$ kJ mol^{-1}

(ii) $\Delta H = 436 + 158 - (2 \times 568) = -542$ kJ mol^{-1}

(c)(i) Activation energy has to be overcome before a reaction can take place. At room temperature, insufficient molecules exceed the activation energy

(ii)

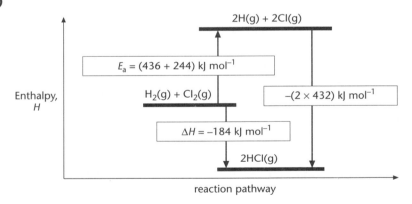

(8) (a) raising the pressure increases the concentration of gas molecules causing an increased rate of collision and faster reaction.

(b)(i) To relieve the effect of increased temperature, the equilibrium moves to the left in the endothermic direction.

(ii) To relieve the effect of increased pressure, the equilibrium moves to the right in the direction that produces fewer gas molecules.

(c) The temperature used is sufficiently high to allow the reaction to occur at a realistic rate, but not too high to give a minimal equilibrium yield of ammonia (equilibrium yield decreases with increasing temperature).

(9) (a) As carbon chain length increases, boiling point increases because van der Waals forces increase between molecules

(b) (i) Each successive member differs by $-CH_2-$ and has the same general formula. The members of a homologous series have the same functional group and react similarly.

(ii) C_nH_{2n+2}

(iii) $C_{15}H_{32}$

(iv) 72

(c) (i) $C_9H_{20} \rightarrow C_6H_{14} + C_3H_6$

(ii) propene

(iii) alkenes are needed to make polymers. Cracking converts hydrocarbons in low demand into shorter chain alkanes in greater demand.

(10) (a)

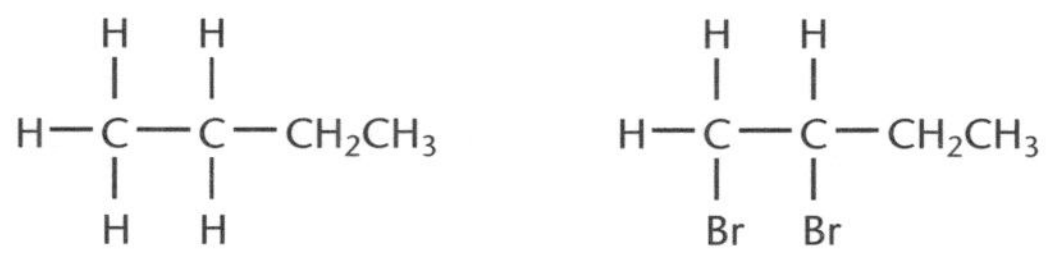

(b) (i) addition

(ii) electrophile

(iii)

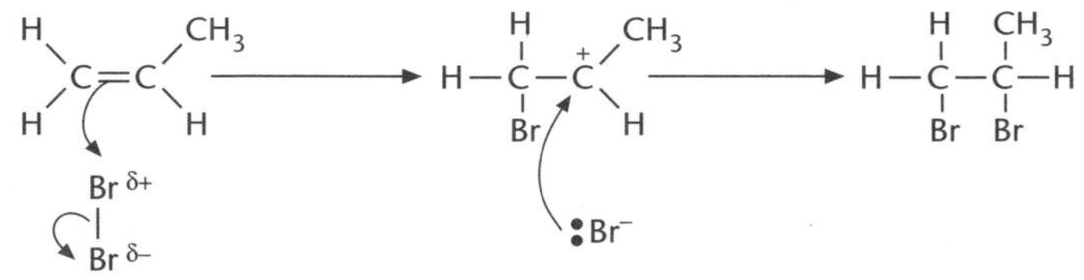

(c)

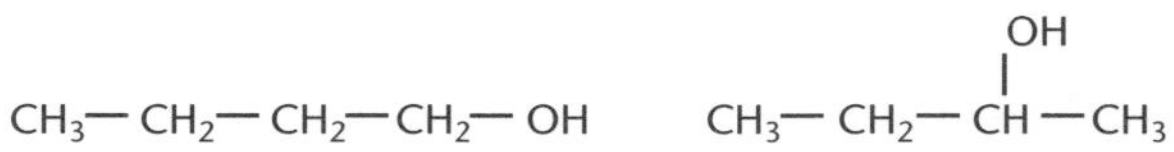

(d) (i) addition

(ii)

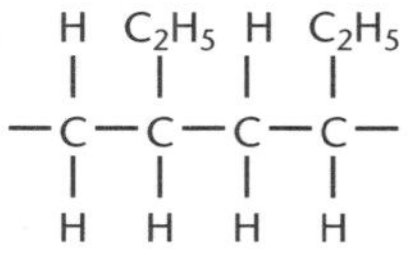

(11)(a) $Cl_2 \rightarrow 2Cl\bullet$
$C_4H_{10} + Cl\bullet \rightarrow C_4H_9\bullet + HCl$
$C_4H_9\bullet + Cl_2 \rightarrow C_4H_9Cl + Cl\bullet$
$2C_4H_9\bullet \rightarrow C_8H_{18}$ or $2Cl\bullet \rightarrow Cl_2$ or $C_4H_9\bullet + Cl\bullet \rightarrow C_4H_9Cl$

(b)(i)   **A**: $CH_3CH_2CH_2CH_2Cl$;   **B**: $CH_3CH_2CH_2CH_2OH$;   **C**: $CH_3CH_2CH_2CHO$

(ii) OH^- behaves as a nucleophile by donating an electron pair

(iii)   from orange to green

(iv) $CH_3CH_2CH_2CH_2OH + [O] \rightarrow CH_3CH_2CH_2CHO + H_2O$

(c)(i)   molar ratio: $Cl \frac{41.6}{35.5} : C \frac{14.0}{12} : F \frac{44.4}{19}$
empirical formula = $ClCF_2$
molecular formula = $Cl_2C_2F_4$

(ii)

1,2-dichloro-1,1,2,2-tetrafluoroethane or 1,1-dichloro-1,2,2,2-tetrafluoroethane

Mock Exam

Answer all the questions   Time: 2 hours

(1) Oxygen and nitrogen monoxide react together to make nitrogen dioxide.

$$O_2(g) + 2NO(g) \rightarrow 2NO_2(g)$$

(a) In a first experiment, [NO(g)] was kept constant whilst [O_2(g)] was varied. The graph below shows how the reaction rate changed for the first experiment.

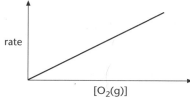

Deduce the order of reaction with respect to O_2. Explain your answer.

order ...... First order ....✓

explanation ...... The rate is directly proportional to ...... ②

...... the concentration of oxygen. Rate ∝ [O_2] ...... **[2]**

(b) In a second experiment, [O_2(g)] was kept constant whilst [NO(g)] was varied. The results showed that the reaction was 2nd order with respect to NO. Show how the rate would change as [NO(g)] was increased on the graph below.

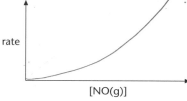

✓ 1

[1]

(c) Deduce the overall order of this reaction.

...... Third order .... **[1]** ✓ 1

rate = [NO]² [O_2]¹

(d) If the concentration of NO was doubled and that of O_2 was halved, what would happen to the reaction rate? Explain your answer.

...... It would double. The rate is equal to: ......

...... rate = [NO]² [O_2]¹   So when NO is doubled the ...... ✓ ②

...... rate is squared, when O_2 is halved the rate is halved. ...... **[2]**

4 × 0.5 = 2, so rate doubles.

(e) Using your answers to **(a)** and **(b)**, write the rate equation for this reaction. ✓ 1

...... Rate = [O_2] [NO]² .... **[1]**

(f) When $[O_2(g)] = 1.0 \times 10^{-2}$ mol dm^{-3} and $[NO(g)] = 3.0 \times 10^{-2}$ mol dm^{-3}, the reaction rate is 6.3×10^{-4} mol dm^{-3} s^{-1}.
Calculate the rate constant for this reaction. State the units.

$$0.00063 = k(0.01 \times 0.03^2)$$

mol dm^{-3} s^{-1} = mol^3 dm^{-9}

mol^2 dm^{-6}

$$0.00063 = 0.000009$$

$$k = \frac{0.00063}{0.000009} = 70$$

$\frac{1}{2}$

$$k = 70 \ dm^6 \ mol^{-2} \ s^{-1}$$

[2]

(g) The reaction rate of 6.3×10^{-4} mol dm^{-3} s^{-1} was measured as the 'rate of disappearance of NO'.

(i) Determine the 'rate of disappearance' of O_2.   Rate at which NO disappears = 0.0006

$$[NO]^2 [O_2]^1$$

$$\therefore \frac{6.3 \times 10^{-4}}{2} = 3.15 \times 10^{-4} = 0.000315 \ mol \ dm^{-3} \ s^{-1}$$

[1]

(ii) Determine the 'rate of appearance' of NO_2.   proportional

$$6.3 \times 10^{-4} \ mol \ dm^{-3} \ s^{-1}$$

[1]

[Total:11]

(2) The equilibrium in the Haber process for the production of ammonia is:

$$N_2(g) + 3H_2(g) \rightleftharpoons 2NH_3(g) \qquad \Delta H = -92 \ kJ \ mol^{-1}$$

1   3   1

Nitrogen and hydrogen were mixed together in a molar ratio of $N_2:H_2 = 1:3$. This mixture was reacted together to produce an equilibrium mixture at 500°C and a total pressure of 800 kPa. The partial pressure of ammonia in the equilibrium mixture was 80 kPa.

(a) Write an expression for K_p for this equilibrium.

$$K_p = \frac{P^2_{NH_3}}{P_{N_2} P^3_{H_2}}$$

✓

[1]

(b) Calculate the partial pressures of nitrogen and hydrogen at equilibrium.

mole fraction × volume = partial pressure

NH_3 $\frac{80}{800} = 0.01$

$800 - 80 = 720$

$1 + 3 = 4$ $\frac{720}{4} = 180$

$H_2 = 180 \times 3 = 540 \ kPa$ ✓

$N_2 = 180 \times 1 = 180 \ kPa$

$NH_3 = 80 kPa$

[2]

(c) Calculate K_p including its units.

$$K_p = \frac{P^2_{NH_3}}{P_{N_2} \, P^3_{H_2}} = \frac{(80)^2}{(180)(540)^3} = 2.26 \times 10^{-7} \, kPa^{-2}$$

[2]

(d) The reaction was repeated at 300°C. By considering the enthalpy change for this reaction, explain what effect this lower temperature would have on:

(i) the equilibrium yield of ammonia

Increase in yield of ammonia as equilibrium in accordance with Le Chatlier's Principle will shift to the right as the reaction is exothermic [2]

(ii) The value of K_p

It would increase, as there would be a higher proportion of ammonia present in the system than before. [2]

(e) **(i)** Predict, using the words **high** or **low**, the conditions of temperature and pressure likely to produce an **optimum** equilibrium yield.

High pressure and low temperature in the system would produce an optimum equilibrium yield. [1]

(ii) Explain why the **actual** conditions used by industry are likely to be different from your answer to **(e)(i)**.

For economic reasons. Although the yield of ammonia produced is greater at lower temperatures, the rate of reaction is also slower so it is not economically viable. Also, it would be costly to use a system that could create such high pressures [2]

[Total:12]

(3) Hydrochloric acid is a strong acid. Potassium hydroxide is a strong base. Benzoic acid, C_6H_5COOH is a weak acid. ($K_a = 6.30 \times 10^{-5}$ mol dm^{-3} at 25°C).

(a) Define pH.

$pH = -\log [H^+]$ [1]

(b)   Calculate the pH of the following at 25°C:
$(K_w = 1.0 \times 10^{-14}$ mol^2 dm$^{-6})$:

(i) 0.20 mol dm^{-3} HCl(aq)

$-\log 0.2 = 0.698970004$

$= 0.7$ (to 1dp)   ✓

[1]

(ii) 0.050 mol dm^{-3} KOH(aq)

$[OH] = \dfrac{1 \times 10^{-14}}{0.05} = 12.68897 = 12.7$ ✓

[2]

(iii) 0.020 mol dm^{-3} C$_6$H$_5$COOH 6.3×10^{-5}

$K_a = \dfrac{[C_6H_5COO^-][H^+]}{C_6H_5COOH}$ $6.3 \times 10^{-5} = \dfrac{[H^+]^2}{0.02}$

$1.26 \times 10^{-6} = [H^+]^2$ $[H^+] = 1.12 \times 10^{-3}$ $pH = -\log[H^+]$
$= -\log 1.12 \times 10^{-3} = 2.949814727$

[3]

$= 2.95$ ✓

(c)   0.050 mol dm^{-3} KOH was titrated against 20 cm^3 0.020 mol dm^{-3}
C$_6$H$_5$COOH until neutralisation took place.

$C_6H_5COOH + KOH \longrightarrow C_6H_5COO^-K^+ + H_2O$ ✓

(i) Write an equation for the reaction between benzoic acid and
hydroxide ions.

$C_6H_5COOH + OH^- \rightleftharpoons C_6H_5COO^- + H_2O$ [1]

(ii) Explain why the hydroxide ions have behaved as a Bronsted–Lowry
base.

Because they act as proton acceptors. They neutralise the

benzoic acid accepting its dissociated H$^+$ ions/protons to   [2]
form water.

(iii) State, with reasons, a suitable indicator for this titration.

phenolphthalein as it works best in alkali pHs.

Equivalence point is within pH range as strong base+weak   [2]
acid.

(iv) The volume of 0.050 mol dm^{-3} KOH needed in this titration is x cm^3.
Calculate the value of x.   volume $= \dfrac{moles}{concentration}$

$\dfrac{20}{1000} \times 0.02 = 0.0004$ volume $= \dfrac{0.0004}{0.05} = 0.008 \times 1000 = \boxed{8 cm^3}$

[2]

(d)   This titration was repeated a second time using $\frac{x}{2}$ cm^3 of
0.050 mol dm^{-3} KOH.

(i) Why would the concentrations of benzoic acid and its conjugate base
be equal to one another?

Because 8cm^3 is needed to fully neutralise the solution to equivalence point,

so half that amount would strike a balance. Because of the   [1]
addition of hydroxide OH$^-$ ions   ✓

(ii) Calculate the pH of this solution.

[2]

[Total: 17]

(4) (a) The table below shows the enthalpy changes in a Born–Haber cycle for the formation of potassium chloride, KCl, from its elements.

Complete the table by writing equations, including state symbols, in the spaces.

Enthalpy change	Equation
atomisation of potassium	$K_{(s)} \longrightarrow K_{(g)}$
1st ionisation energy of potassium	$K_{(g)} \longrightarrow K^+_{(g)} + e^-$
atomisation of chlorine	$Cl_{2(g)} \longrightarrow 2Cl_{(g)}$
electron affinity of chlorine	$Cl_{(g)} + e^- \quad Cl^-_{(g)}$
lattice enthalpy of potassium chloride	$K^+_{(g)} + Cl^-_{(g)} \longrightarrow KCl_{(s)}$
formation of potassium chloride	$K_{(s)} + \frac{1}{2}Cl_{2(g)} \longrightarrow KCl_{(s)}$

[6]

(b) The lattice enthalpy of KCl is -718 kJ mol^{-1} but that of NaCl is -788 kJ mol^{-1}.

(i) Define the term *lattice enthalpy*.

The energy required to form one mole of an ionic lattice from its constituent gaseous ions.

[2]

(ii) Suggest why there is a difference between these lattice enthalpies.

Na^+ ion has a greater charge density than K^+ ion as Na^+ ion has a smaller ionic radius than K^+ ion so can get closer to Cl^- ion.

[2]

[Total: 10]

(5) Each of the answers to parts **(a)** and **(b)** of this question uses **one of the oxides below**. You can use each oxide once, more than once or not at all.

Oxides: Na_2O; MgO; SiO_2; SO_3

(a) identify an oxide from the list above that:

(i) reacts with water forming a strongly alkaline solution ....Na_2O........ **[1]**

(ii) is insoluble in water ....SiO_2........ **[1]**

(iii) is slightly soluble in water forming a weakly alkaline solution ...MgO... **[1]**

(iv) reacts vigorously with water forming a strongly acidic solution ...SO_3 **[1]**

(v) has a simple molecular structure at room temperature ....SO_3........ **[1]**

(b) Suggest equations for the reaction of water with one of the oxides in the list above to form

(i) an acidic solution

.... $SO_3 + H_2O \rightarrow H_2SO_4$ .... **[1]**

(ii) an alkaline solution

.... $Na_2O + H_2O \rightarrow 2NaOH$ .... **[1]**

(c) Suggest an equation for the reaction that would take place if the two solutions in **(b)** were mixed together.

.... $H_2SO_4 + 2NaOH \rightarrow Na_2SO_4 + 2H_2O$ .... **[1]**

(d) (i) State and explain the trend in the oxidation number shown in the **highest** oxides of the elements Na to Cl across Period 3 of the Periodic Table.

trend ....

explanation ....

.... **[2]**

(ii) Predict the formula of the **highest** oxide of chlorine.

.... **[1]**

[Total: 11]

(6) (a) Complete the table below to show the oxidation state of the **transition metal**.

Species	$Cr_2O_7{}^{2-}$	$[CuCl_4]^{2-}$	$VO(H_2O)_5]^{2+}$
oxidation state	+6	+2	+4

[3]

(b) State **two** examples of the use of transition elements as catalysts in industrial processes.

Iron in Haber Process

Vanadium Oxide in Contact Process [2]

(c) State **two** properties that are typical of a transition element.

Variable oxidation states

Can form coloured complex ions [2]

(d) Complete the electronic configuration of:

(i) an iron atom, Fe, $1s^2\ 2s^2\ 2p^6\ 3s^2\ 3p^6\ 3d^6\ 4s^2$

(ii) an iron(II) ion, Fe^{2+} $1s^2\ 2s^2\ 2p^6\ 3s^2\ 3p^6\ 3d^6$ [2]

(e) Iron(II) ions form aqueous solutions containing the complex ion $[Fe(H_2O)_6]^{2+}$

State the likely shape and bond angles of $[Fe(H_2O)_6]^{2+}$

shape Octahedral

bond angles $90°$ [2]

(f) Use the data given below to answer the questions which follow.:

$$14H^+(aq) + Cr_2O_7{}^{2-}(aq) + 6e^- \rightleftharpoons 2Cr^{3+}(aq) + 7H_2O(l) \quad E^\ominus = +1.33\ V$$
$$Fe^{3+}(aq) + e^- \rightleftharpoons Fe^{2+}(aq) \quad E^\ominus = +0.77\ V$$
$$8H^+(aq) + FeO_4{}^{2-}(aq) + 3e^- \rightleftharpoons Fe^{3+}(aq) + 4H_2O(l) \quad E^\ominus = +2.20\ V$$
$$4H^+(aq) + VO_3{}^-(aq) + e^- \rightleftharpoons VO^{2+}(aq) + 2H_2O(l) \quad E^\ominus = +1.00\ V$$
$$8H^+(aq) + MnO_4{}^-(aq) + 5e^- \rightleftharpoons Mn^{2+}(aq) + 4H_2O(l) \quad E^\ominus = +1.52\ V$$

(i) Which transition metal species shown above is the most powerful oxidising agent?

$FeO_4{}^{2-}$ [1]

(ii) Identify **two** transition metal species which could be used to reduce acidified dichromate(VI) ions.

species 1 ..... Fe^{2+} .....

species 2 ..... VO^{2+} ..... [2]

(iii) Construct an overall equation to show the reaction of acidified dichromate(VI) with **one** of the species that you have chosen in (ii)

..... $Cr_2O_7^{2-} + 6Fe^{2+} + 14H^+ \rightleftharpoons 2Cr^{3+} + 6Fe^{3+} + 7H_2O$ ..... [1]

[Total: 15]

(7) Examine the reaction scheme below.

$CuSO_4(s)$ —$H_2O(l)$→ blue solution **A** —dil $NH_3(aq)$→ blue precipitate **C**

A —excess conc HCl(aq)→ yellow-green solution **B**

C —excess conc $NH_3(aq)$→ deep blue solution **D**

(a) State the formula of each of the species in the products lettered **A** to **D**.

Formula of **A**: ..... $Cu(H_2O)_4^{2+}$ .....

Formula of **B**: ..... $CuCl_4^{2-}$ .....

Formula of **C**: ..... $[Cu(OH)_2(H_2O)_4]$ .....

Formula of **D**: ..... $[Cu(H_2O)_2(NH_3)_4]^{2+}$ ..... [4]

(b) This part refers to the conversion of **A** and **B**.

(i) State the type of reaction that converts **A** into **B**.

..... Ligand substitution ..... [1]

(ii) Write the equation for the conversion of **A** into **B**.

..... $Cu(H_2O)_4 + 4Cl^- \rightleftharpoons CuCl_4^{2-} + 4H_2O$ ..... [1]

(iii) State the shape of **B**.

..... Tetrahedral ..... [1]

(c) Sulphur dioxide gas was bubbled through the yellow-green solution of compound **B**. The colourless species $CuCl_2^-$ is formed together with SO_4^{2-} ions.

(i) Identify the oxidation state of copper in $CuCl_2^-$.

..... +1 ..... [1]

(ii) Deduce the role of sulphur dioxide in the conversion of **B** into $CuCl_2^-$.

Reduces Cu^{2+} to Cu^+ [1]

(iii) Explain, in terms of electronic configurations, why **B** is coloured but $CuCl_2^-$ is colourless.

Because $CuCl_2^-$ contains the Cu^+ ion which still has an electron in the $4s$ orbital and a full $3d$ orbital ^So the electrons in the $3d$ orbital does not absorb different visible wavelengths of light but in Cu^{2+} incomplete $3d$ 'splits' and absorbs different wavelengths of light as electrons are promoted and fall back down visible light (spectrum seen) emitted. orbital full [3]

(d) When water is added to **B**, a blue solution is obtained. Write an equation for this reaction.

$CuCl_4^{2-} + 4H_2O \underset{}{\overset{H^+}{\rightleftharpoons}} Cu(H_2O)_4^{2+} + 4Cl^-$ [1]

[Total: 13]

(8) Methylbenzene, $C_6H_5CH_3$, is nitrated in a similar way to benzene. The organic compound formed is 4-nitromethylbenzene.

(a) Draw the structure of 4-nitromethylbenzene.

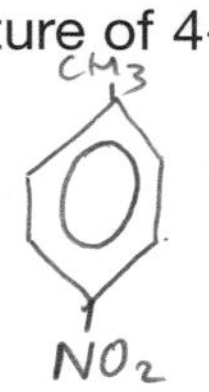

[1]

(b) **(i)** State the reagents for this reaction.

Concentrated Sulphuric acid and concentrated nitric acid [2]

(ii) Name the type of mechanism.

Electrophilic substitution (E) [1]

(iii) Describe, with the aid of curly arrows, the mechanism of the reaction between the nitronium ion, NO_2^+, and methylbenzene.

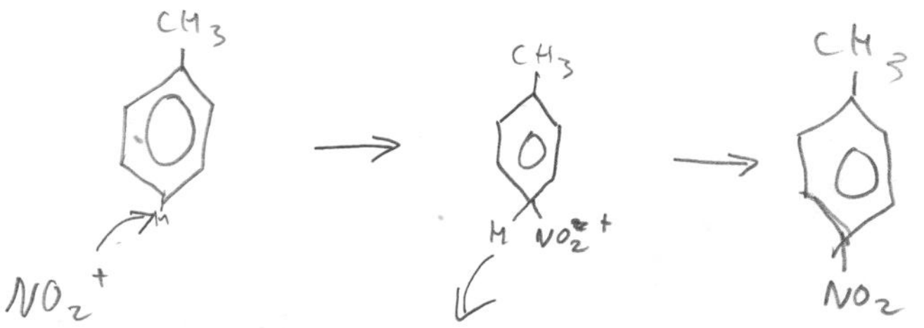

[3]

(c) 4-Nitromethylbenzene was converted to 4-aminobenzenecarboxylic acid by the two-stage synthesis shown.

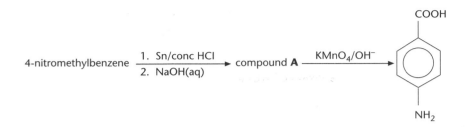

(i) Identify compound **A** and show its structure below.

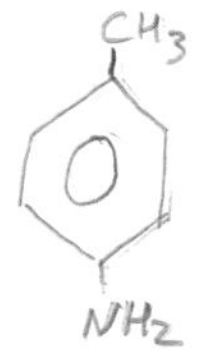

[a hand-drawn benzene ring with CH_3 at the top and NH_2 at the bottom]

[1]

(ii) Suggest why NaOH(aq) is used in the first stage of this synthesis.

To neutralise excess H⁺ ions from hydrochloric acid to prevent them reacting with 4-amino methyl benzene [1]

(iii) Construct a balanced equation for the second stage of this synthesis. You can represent the oxidising agent, KMnO₄/OH⁻, as [O].

$$C_6H_5CH_3NH_2 + 3[O] \longrightarrow C_6H_5CO_2HNH_2 + H_2O$$

[1]

(d) 4-Aminobenzenecarboxylic acid can be polymerised.

(i) State, with a reason, the type of polymerisation that takes place.

Condensation polymerisation, as water is formed when two monomer units join [2]

(ii) Draw a diagram below to show a short section of the polymer formed. Clearly show the repeat unit of the polymer.

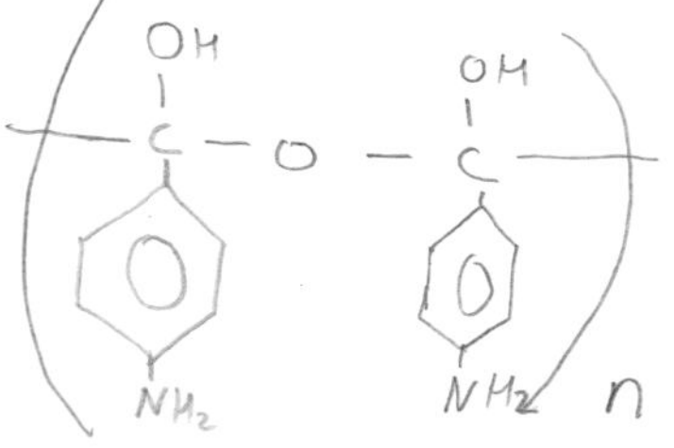

[hand-drawn polymer structure showing two benzene rings each with NH_2 group, connected via $C-O$ linkage with OH groups, bracketed with subscript n]

[2]

[Total: 14]

(9) Cinnamaldehyde is the main flavouring agent in oil of cinnamon.

(a) Cinnamaldehyde has two stereoisomers and one of these is shown below.

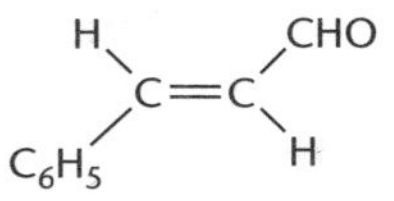

(i) What is the molecular formula of cinnamaldehyde?

.... $C_9 H_8 O$ .... **[1]**

(ii) What type of stereoisomerism is shown by cinnamaldehyde?

.... geometric isomerism .... **[1]**

(iii) Draw a diagram to show clearly the other stereoisomer of cinnamaldehyde.

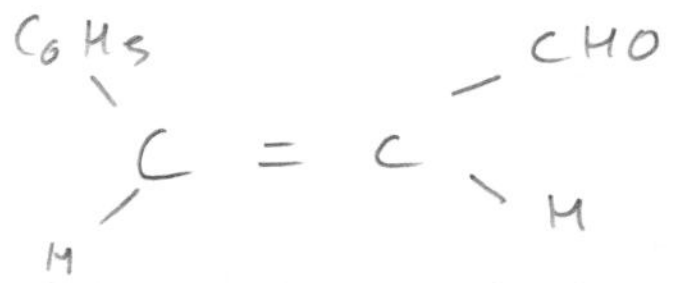

[1]

(iv) Explain how this stereoisomerism arises.

.... No free rotation about the double bond

.... so stereoisomerism possible .... **[2]**

(b) Cinnamaldehyde reacts with hydrogen bromide HBr to form a mixture of two structural isomers **A** and **B**.

(i) Draw the structures of compounds **A** and **B**.

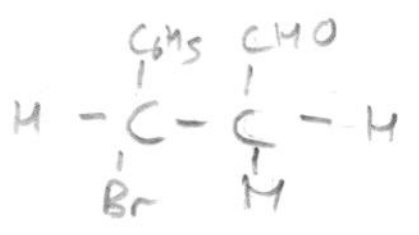

compound **A**

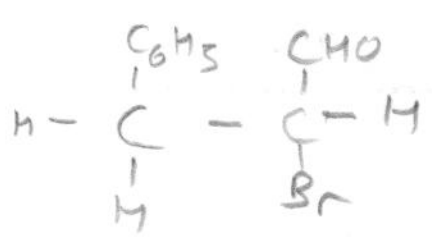

compound **B**

[2]

(ii) Name this type of reaction.

.... Electrophilic Addition reaction .... **[1]**

(iii) Explain why compounds **A** and **B** each have optical isomers.

Have a chiral carbon atom so can rotate the plane of polarised light. **[1]**

(iv) Draw diagrams to show clearly the optical isomers of **either** compound **A** or compound **B**.

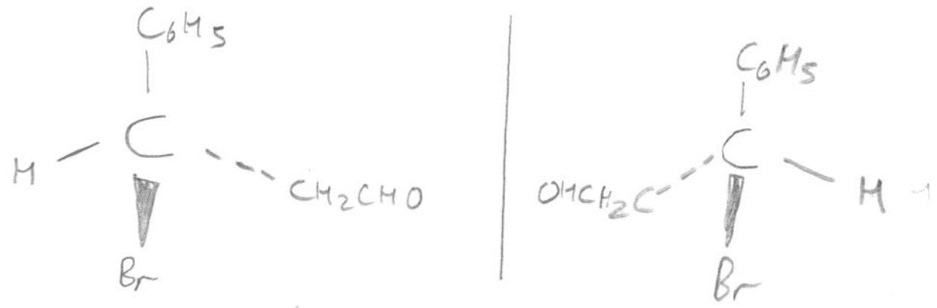

[2]

(c) Cinnamaldehyde can be polymerised. Draw a diagram below to show a short section of the polymer formed. Clearly show the repeat unit of the polymer.

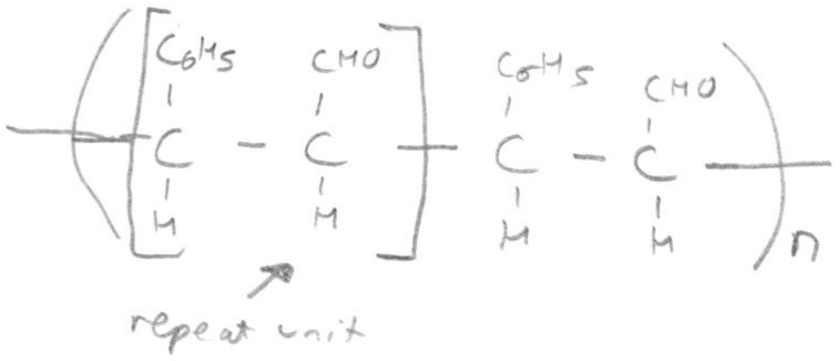

repeat unit

[2]

(d) A chemist wanted to prepare the compounds **C** and **D** shown below.

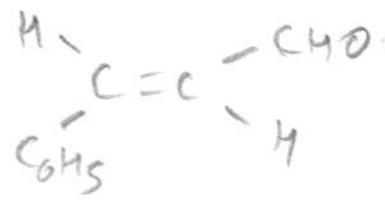

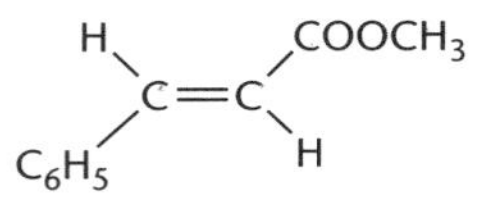

compound **C** 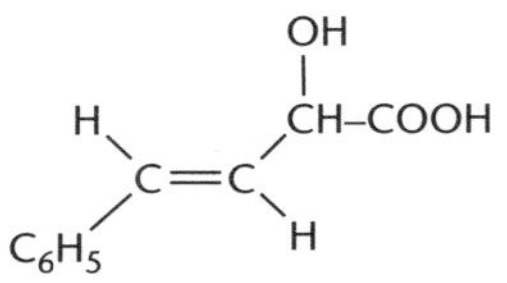   compound **D**

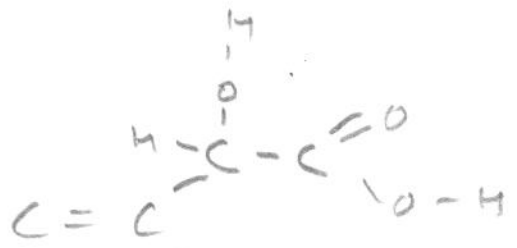

Suggest synthetic routes that could be used to prepare compounds **C** and **D** from cinnamaldehyde.
For each reaction in your schemes:
• state the reagents and conditions
• draw the structure of any intermediate compounds
• write balanced equations.

For compound C, react cinnamaldehyde with sulphuric acid and sodium dichromate (VI) while refluxing/heat to get $H-C=C-CO_2H$ ... React this with methanol using an acid catalyst like sulphuric acid to get compound C

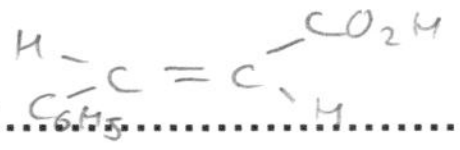

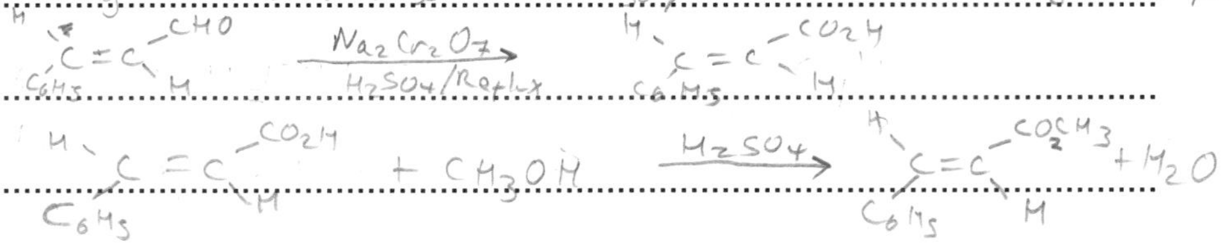

....

....

....

....

....

.... **[14]**

[Total: 27]

(10) The structures of two isomers with the molecular formula $C_3H_6O_3$ are shown below.

$$CH_3CHOHCOOH \qquad HOCH_2CH_2COOH$$

Show how n.m.r. spectroscopy could be used to distinguish between these two isomers.

For each isomer, you should predict:
• the number of peaks in its n.m.r. spectrum corresponding to the different types of proton
• the number of each different type of proton
• spin-spin coupling patterns

CH₃CHOHCOOH would show 4 peaks at a ratio of
3:1:1:1 . HOCH₂CH₂COOH would show 4 peaks
at a ratio of 1:2:2:1
CH₃CHOHCOOH would have a one singlet, 1 quartet, 1 doublet
HOCH₂CH₂COOH would have 2 triplets and 2 singlets

....

....

....

....

[Total 10]

Answers

(1) (a) 1st order as the rate is proportional to the concentration.

(b)

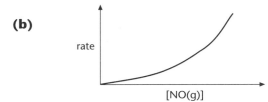

(c) 3rd order.

(d) rate doubles. Effect of NO is ×4; Effect of O_2 is $\frac{1}{2}$; Overall effect $= \frac{4}{2} = 2$

(e) rate $= k[NO]^2[O_2]$

(f) $k = 70.0 \ dm^6 \ mol^{-2} \ s^{-1}$

(g) (i) $3.15 \times 10^{-4} \ mol \ dm^{-3} \ s^{-1}$

   (ii) $6.30 \times 10^{-4} \ mol \ dm^{-3} \ s^{-1}$

(2) (a) $K_p = \dfrac{p_{NH_3}{}^2}{p_{N_2} \times p_{H_2}{}^3}$

(b) $p_{N_2} = \dfrac{1}{4} \times 720 = 180 \ kPa^*; \quad p_{H_2} = \dfrac{3}{4} \times 720 = 540 \ kPa$

(c) $K_p = \dfrac{80^2}{180 \times 540^3} = 2.26 \times 10^{-7} \ kPa^{-2}$

(d) (i) Greater equilibrium yield of ammonia because lower temperatures favour exothermic direction.

   (ii) K_p would be increased because a change in temperature alters K_p. The yield of ammonia increases so K_p increases.

(e) (i) Low temperature and high pressure.

   (ii) Low temperatures may reduce the reaction rate. High pressures may be impracticable because of the expense of compression and the thick walls of containers required to withstand high pressure.

(3) (a) $pH = -\log_{10}[H^+(aq)]$

(b) (i) 0.7

   (ii) 12.7

   (iii) 2.95

(c) (i) $C_6H_5COOH + OH^- \rightarrow C_6H_5COO^- + H_2O$

   (ii) A Bronsted–Lowry base gains a proton $OH^- + H^+ \rightarrow H_2O$

    (iii) Phenolphthalein, because the combination is a strong base and weak acid.

    (iv) 8 cm^3

(d)(i) The reaction has been 'half-neutralised'.

    (ii) 4.20

(4) **(a)(i)**

Enthalpy change	Equation
atomisation of potassium	$K(s) \rightarrow K(g)$
1st ionisation energy of potassium	$K(g) \rightarrow K^+(g) + e^-$
atomisation of chlorine	$\frac{1}{2}Cl_2(g) \rightarrow Cl(g)$
electron affinity of chlorine	$Cl(g) + e^- \rightarrow Cl^-(g)$
lattice enthalpy	$K^+(g) + Cl^-(g) \rightarrow KCl(s)$
formation of potassium chloride	$K(s) + \frac{1}{2}Cl_2(g) \rightarrow KCl(s)$

  (b)(i) The lattice enthalpy of an ionic compound is the enthalpy change that accompanies the formation of 1 mole of an ionic compound from its constituent gaseous ions.

    (ii) From NaCl to KCl, the ionic size of the cation increases, charge density decreases, attraction between ions decreases.

(5) **(a)(i)** Na_2O

    (ii) SiO_2

  (iii) MgO

   (iv) SO_3

    (v) SO_3

  (b)(i) $SO_3 + H_2O \rightarrow H_2SO_4$

    (ii) $Na_2O + H_2O \rightarrow 2NaOH$

(c) $2NaOH + H_2SO_4 \rightarrow Na_2SO_4 + 2H_2O$

(d)(i) The oxidation number increases by one for each successive element across Period 3. The number of outer shell electrons that can be involved in bonding also increases by one for each successive element across the Period.

    (ii) Cl_2O_7

(6) (a)

species	$Cr_2O_7^{2-}$	$[CuCl_4]^{2-}$	$VO(H_2O)_5]^{2+}$
oxidation state	+6	+2	+4

(b) V_2O_5 is used in the Contact process for the production of sulphuric acid. Fe in Haber process in the production of ammonia.

(c) Coloured compounds; compounds with variable oxidation states.

(d) (i) an iron atom, Fe, $\quad 1s^2\ 2s^2\ 2p^6\ 3s^2\ 3p^6\ 3d^6\ 4s^2$

(ii) an iron(II) ion, Fe^{2+} $\quad 1s^2\ 2s^2\ 2p^6\ 3s^2\ 3p^6\ 3d^6$

(e) (i) Octahedral shape; 90° bond angle.

(f) (i) $FeO_4^{2-}(aq)$

(ii) $VO^{2+}(aq)$ and $Fe^{2+}(aq)$

(iii) $6Fe^{2+}(aq) + Cr_2O_7^{2-}(aq) + 14H^+(aq) \rightarrow 6Fe^{3+}(aq) + 2Cr^{3+}(aq) + 7H_2O(l)$

(7) (a) **A**, $[Cu(H_2O)_6]^{2+}$; **B**, $CuCl_4^{2-}$; **C**, $Cu(OH)_2(H_2O)_4$; **D**, $[Cu(NH_3)_4(H_2O)_2]^{2+}$

(b) (i) Ligand substitution.

(ii) $[Cu(H_2O)_6]^{2+}(aq) + 4Cl^-(aq) \rightarrow CuCl_4^{2-}(aq) + 6H_2O(l)$

(iii) Tetrahedral.

(c) (i) +1

(ii) Reducing agent.

(iii) $CuCl_4^{2-}$ has a partially filled 3d sub-shell ($3d^9$). $CuCl_2^-$ has a full 3d sub-shell ($3d^{10}$). Electronic transitions between d orbital electrons are only possible for $CuCl_4^{2-}$.

(d) $CuCl_4^{2-}(aq) + 6H_2O(l) \rightarrow [Cu(H_2O)_6]^{2+}(aq) + 4Cl^-(aq)$

(8) (a)

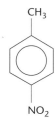

(b) (i) Concentrated HNO_3 and concentrated H_2SO_4.

(ii) Electrophilic substitution

(iii)

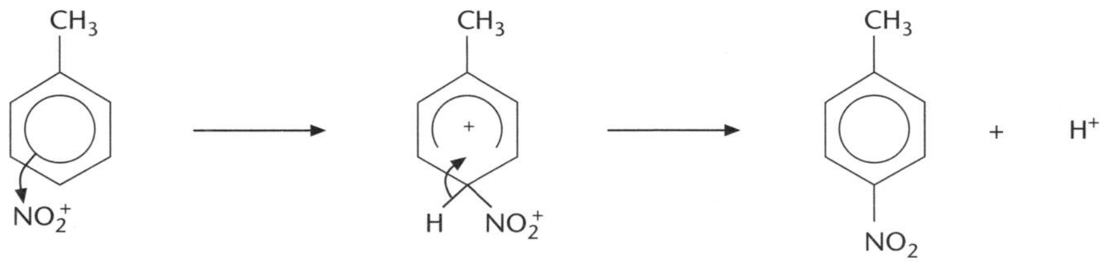

(c) (i)

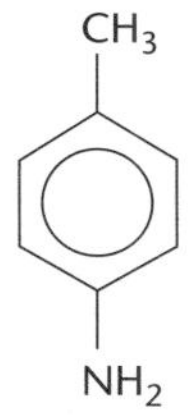

4-aminomethylbenzene

(ii) To neutralise the amine salt, $H_3C-C_6H_4-NH_3{}^+Cl^-$ formed from the presence of concentrated HCl.

(iii)

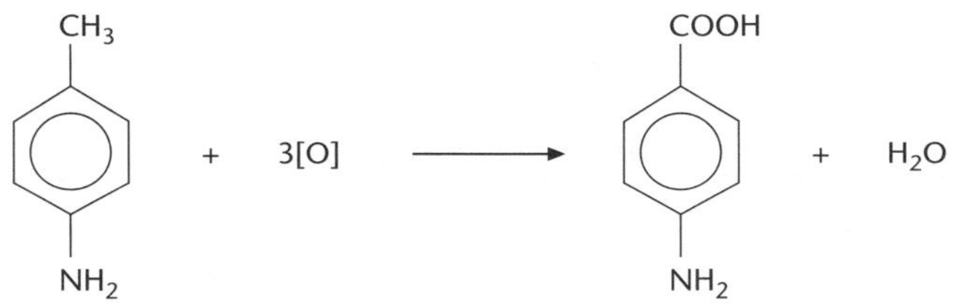

(d) (i) Condensation polymerisation because water is formed when each pair of monomer units join.

(ii)

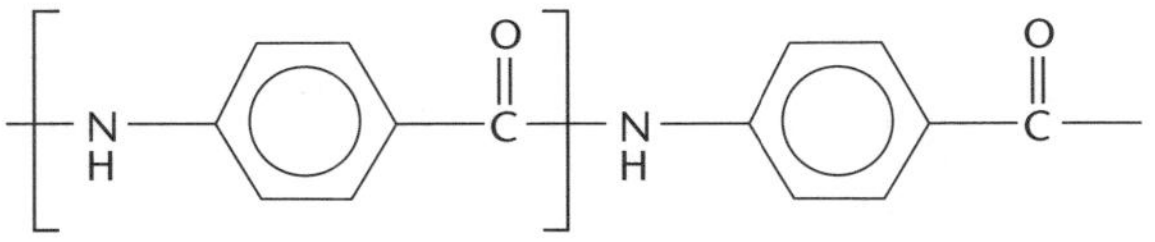

(9) (a) (i) C_9H_8O

(ii) *cis–trans* isomerism

(iii)

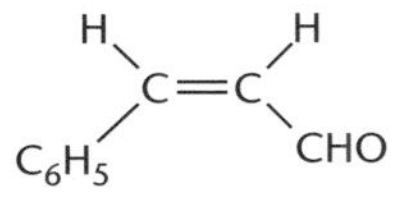

(iv) Two different groups are attached to each end of double bond which prevents rotation.

(b) (i)

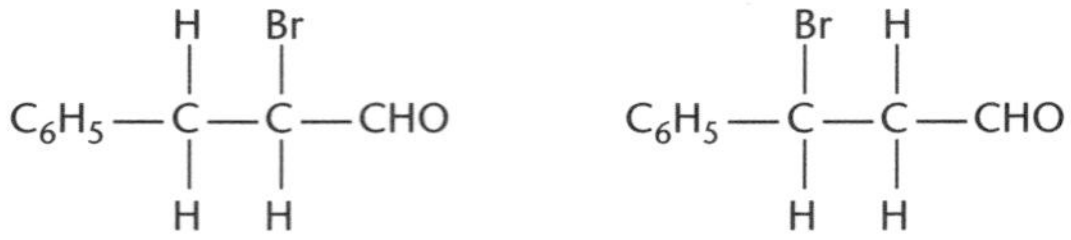

(ii) Electrophilic addition

(iii) They both have a chiral or asymmetric carbon atom.

(iv)

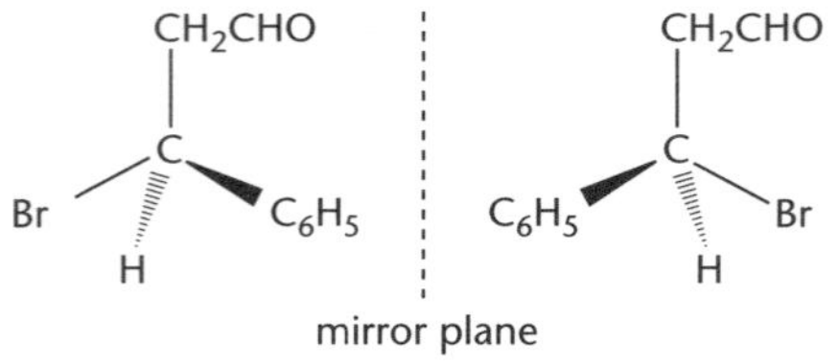

mirror plane

(c)

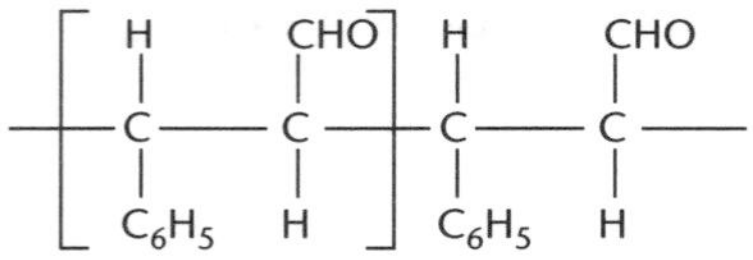

(d) Compound **C**

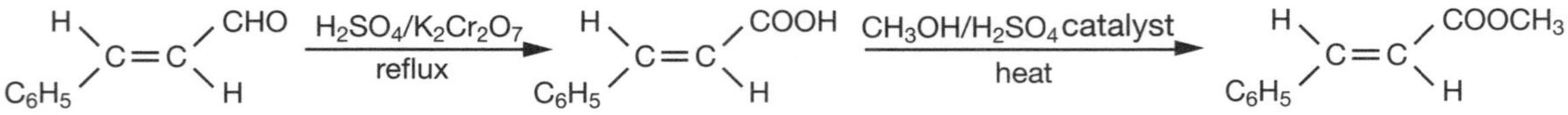

$C_6H_5CH{=}CHCHO + [O] \rightarrow C_6H_5CH{=}CHCOOH$

$C_6H_5CH{=}CHCOOH + CH_3OH \rightarrow C_6H_5CH{=}CHCOOCH_3 + H_2O$

Compound **D**

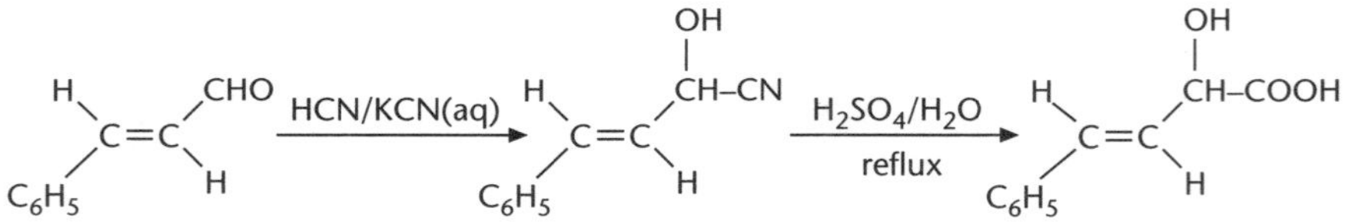

$C_6H_5CH{=}CHCHO + HCN \rightarrow C_6H_5CH{=}CHCHOHCN$

$C_6H_5CH{=}CHCHOHCN + 2H_2O + H^+ \rightarrow C_6H_5CH{=}CHCHOHCOOH + NH_4^+$

(10) $CH_3CHOHCOOH$

Different types of proton: 4

Number of each type: CH_3 (3); CH (1); OH (1); COOH (1)

Spin-spin coupling: CH_3, doublet; CH, quartet; OH and COOH, singlets

$HOCH_2CH_2COOH$

Different types of proton: 4

Number of each type: HO (1); OCH_2 (2); CH_2 (2); COOH (1)

Spin-spin coupling: HO and COOH, singlets; OCH_2, triplet; CH_2, triplet

Periodic Table

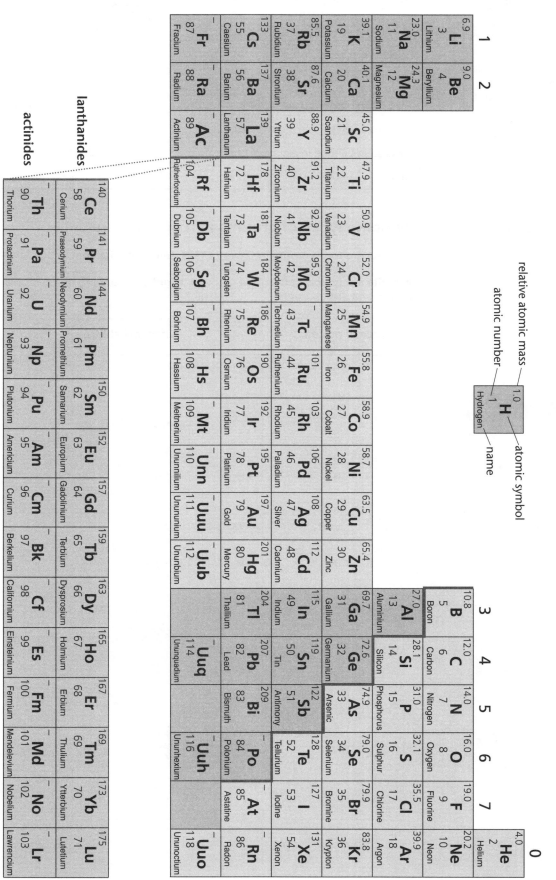

The Periodic Table

Spectral data

Characteristic infra-red absorptions in organic molecules

bond	location	wavenumber
C—O	alcohols, esters	$1000 - 1300$ cm^{-1}
C=O	aldehydes, ketones, carboxylic acids, esters	$1680 - 1750$ cm^{-1}
O—H	hydrogen bonded in caboxylic acids	$2500 - 3300$ cm^{-1} (broad)
N—H	primary amines	$3100 - 3500$ cm^{-1}
O—H	hydrogen bonded in alcohols, phenols	$3230 - 3550$ cm^{-1}
C—H	free	$3580 - 3670$ cm^{-1}

Chemical shifts for some types of protons in n.m.r. spectra

- Chemical shifts are for hydrogen relative to TMS (tetramethylsilane).

- Chemical shifts are typical values and can vary slightly depending on the solvent, concentration and substituents.

type of proton	chemical shift, δ
R–CH$_3$	0.7–1.6
R–CH$_2$–R	1.2–1.4
R$_3$CH	1.6–2.0
$-\overset{O}{\underset{\|\|}{C}}-CH_3$ $-\overset{O}{\underset{\|\|}{C}}-CH_2$–R	2.0–2.9
⬡–CH$_3$ ⬡–CH$_2$–R	2.3–2.7
—O—CH$_3$ —O—CH$_2$–R	3.3–4.3
R–OH	3.5–5.5
⬡–OH	6.5–7.0
⬡–H	7.1–7.7
R$-\overset{O}{\underset{\|\|}{C}}-$H ⬡$-\overset{O}{\underset{\|\|}{C}}-$H	9.5–10
$-\overset{O}{\underset{\|\|}{C}}-$OH	11.0–11.7